CICHLIDS

Robert J. Goldstein, Ph.D.

Biology Department
Emory University
Atlanta, Georgia

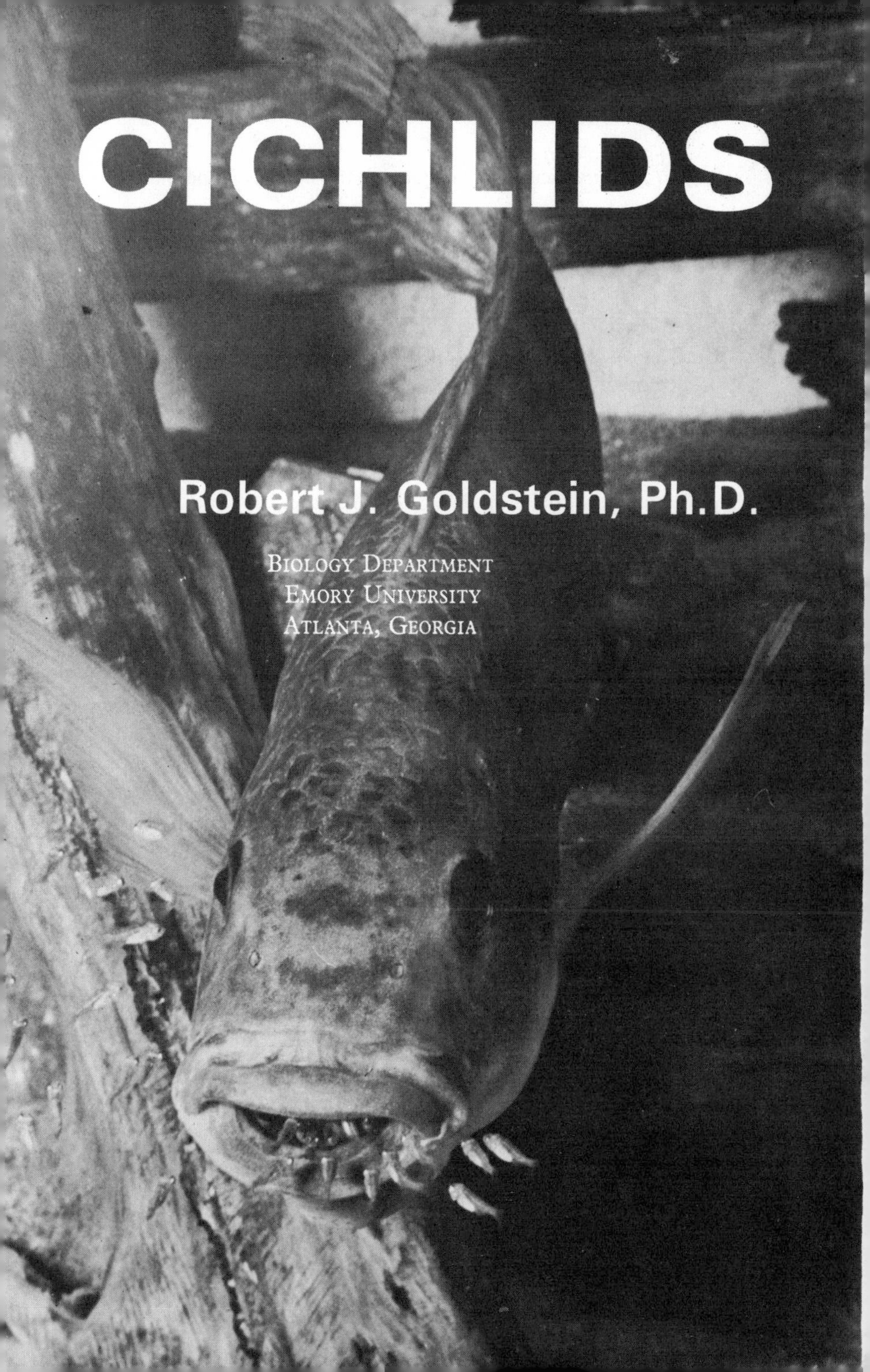

Cover: *Pelmatochromis taeniatus*. Photo by H. Hansen.

Frontispiece:
Tilapia fry fleeing to sanctuary in the mouth of a parent.

ILLUSTRATIONS

American Museum of Natural History, 27, top 40;

Dr. Herbert R. Axelrod, 17, top 33, bottom 40, top 42, bottom 48, bottom 65, top 75, 76, 77, top 104, bottom 105, top 108, top 113, 124, 133, 143, top 145, top 149, bottom 152, 153, top 156, bottom 157, top 161, bottom 164, 165, 168, 169, 172, 173, 176, 177, bottom 183, top 184, 185, bottom 192, bottom 196, top 199, bottom 200, top 201, 202, 203, top 206, bottom 208, bottom 212, bottom 225;

E. A. Baumbach, 129;

Wolfgang Bechtle, 45;

Gerhard Budich, 30, 170, 171, 174, 175, 178, 179;

Milan Chvojka, 71, 135, bottom 139;

D. H. Eccles, 84;

Stanislav Frank, bottom 125, bottom 145, bottom 161, top 209;

Robert J. Goldstein, 24, bottom 36, 87, 94, 95, 96, 98, 132, 191, bottom 199, bottom 220, 223;

Hilmar Hansen, bottom 14, top 36, 41, top 57, top 65, 69, top 72, 78, 80, 88, 89, top 92, 93, top 97, 101, bottom 104, bottom 108, 109, 114, bottom 148, bottom 156, top 157, 160, 181, 194, top 212, 213, top 220;

Wilhelm Hoppe, 6, bottom 92, 100, 103, top 105, 110, 111, 112, bottom 113, 115, 121;

ISBN 0-87666-020-0
H-939   Cichlids (Goldstein)

Distributed in the U.S.A. by T.F.H. Publications, Inc., 211 West Sylvania Avenue, P.O. Box 27, Neptune City, N.J. 07753; in England by T.F.H. (Gt. Britain) Ltd., 13 Nutley Lane, Reigate, Surrey; in Canada to the book store and library trade by Clarke, Irwin & Company, Clarwin House, 791 St. Clair Avenue West, Toronto 10, Ontario; in Canada to the pet trade by Rolf C. Hagen Ltd., 3225 Sartelon Street, Montreal 382, Quebec; in Southeast Asia by Y.W. Ong, 9 Lorong 36 Geylang, Singapore 14; in Australia and the south Pacific by Pet Imports Pty. Ltd., P.O. Box 149, Brookvale 2100, N.S.W., Australia. Published by T.F.H. Publications, Inc. Ltd., The British Crown Colony of Hong Kong.

Dr. William T. Innes, bottom 33, top 164;

J. Kassanyi, top 22, 51;

Karl Knaack, 44, bottom 57, bottom 61, 73;

Kremser, bottom 229;

Lincoln Littrell (Line Drawings), 15, 83, 234

Gerhard Marcuse, 1, 10, top 14, 19, 20, 37, 38, 46, 79, 86, top 90, bottom 97, 116, 117, 123, 130, 150, bottom 188, 190, bottom 198, 204, 205, 207, 210, 214;

Muller-Schmida, bottom 90;

A. F. Orsini, 85;

Klaus Paysan, 13, 47, top 48, 159;

Laurence E. Perkins, 127, 151, 167

Photo Tropica, 74, bottom 75;

Dean Quarnstrom, 131;

Rauberbande, 221;

H. J. Richter, 56, 60, 64, 68, 140, 141, top 144;

Roberts Fish Farm, top 188;

Mervin F. Roberts, top 125;

E. Roloff, 43, 58, top 61;

Dr. Eduard Schmidt, bottom 184, bottom 201;

Dr. Gottfried Schubert, 234;

Harald Schultz, 126, 128, bottom 137, 147, top 152, top 187, bottom 192, 193, top 196, 197, top 200, bottom 209, top 215, bottom 224, top 225;

Gunter Senfft, 11, top 55, bottom 215;

Hassie Smith, 162;

Jiri Taborsky, 180;

Tierfrieunde, 189;

G. J. M. Timmerman, 9, bottom 42, 54, 155, 163, bottom 187, 195, bottom 206, 211;

A. van den Nieuwenhuizen, 106, 107, bottom 120, top 139, 142, top 148;

Gene Wolfsheimer, 26, 182, top 183;

Ruda Zukal, 12, 21, bottom 22, 49, 52, 53, bottom 55, 63, bottom 72, 118, top 120, 136, top 137, top 198, top 208, 216, 217, 218, top 224, 228, top 229, 232, 233, 236, 237;

ACKNOWLEDGMENTS

Although I have bred and raised a number of species of cichlids, I am by no means one of this country's outstandingly successful aquarists. There are many far better than I am. Furthermore, I am a parasitologist, not an ichthyologist, and so I write not as a 'Doctor' but as an aquarist. There are a number of leading cichlid aquarists in this country who have contributed enormously to my knowledge of this group of fishes, and almost everything in this book may in some measure be traced back to their guidance, either through correspondence or their publications. I wish to acknowledge these magnificent aquarists: *Dick Stratton, Guy Jordan, Al Klee, Kappy Sprenger, Dr. Henry Lee, Paul Loiselle,* and *Gene Wolfsheimer.* Many behavioral biologists and psychologists have also had a profound effect on our knowledge, and they will be found frequently cited in the bibliography.

Special thanks are due Stratton and Jordan, who critically read the manuscript, and extricated my foot from my mouth embarrassingly often.

There has never been an error-free aquarium book written, and this will be no exception. These errors reflect general misinformation in the hobby, as well as my own limitations. It is the responsibility of every aquarist to critically read, not to blindly accept, the material presented here. Frequent attacks mean that we are engaged in dialogue, and that is the most delicious fruit of research.

—R.J.G. May 28, 1969

CONTENTS

INTRODUCTION

Cichlids have always been the most desirable egg-laying fishes in the aquarium hobby. Their personality, diversity, coloration, and size have appealed to generations of aquarists. How many of us remember that trip to the home of the serious aquarist, where we first saw the layout, productivity, and magnificent specimens of the skilled breeder? The sight of countless young schooling past the air stone or enveloping the parents in a cloud has always thrilled the novice, and no doubt always will. And one is always more and more respectful of the proud aquarist who displays his giant pairs of angels, dempseys, ports, or oscars. We never quite figure out how he has raised such huge fish in such small quarters. And no matter how old we get, or how long in the hobby, there is always that magnificent pair of something to awe us even more.

Petrochromis fasciolatus, an infrequently seen African cichlid species. The great variety of shapes and colors and modes of behavior among cichlids, even the more commonly available species, has made cichlids among the favorites in the aquarium hobby.

In recent years the aquarium hobby has been experiencing ever higher peaks of knowledge and activity, and cichlids have figured handsomely in practically every aspect of aquariology. Indeed, the impetus for the opening up of Africa on a scale never before seen was largely the result of pressure exercised by serious aquarists seeking new and beautiful cichlids. Recently, a group of such aquarists organized themselves into the *American Cichlid Association*, a name perhaps phonetically inappropriate, but literally as pertinent to the hobby of today as any term could be. Some of the great names of the hobby formed the nucleus of this elite group, a group which is certain to swell in numbers as its work makes better aquarists of us all. And so the time seems ripe for us to step back from all this frenetic activity, and take stock of what has happened to this aspect of our hobby. What are the cichlids of today, and how do they differ from the cichlids of yesterday? What great solutions have been finally found, and what new problems have arisen to plague us? Do we know more, or do we just have more information to confuse us? Have we at last achieved the total picture of the cichlids of the world, or have we just risen high enough to have a better view of the long road ahead? This book is designed to attempt to answer these questions on the basis of present knowledge, and the best way to do that is to review the cichlids of the hobby as well as those not yet (and perhaps never) in aquaria, from the standpoint of the aquarist, the taxonomist, the evolutionist, the psychologist, the biologist, and the dealer. This book is not designed for skimming, or for looking up a particular species. It's for reading from cover to cover, not once, but as often as you need to do it. This is an effort to take the cumulative knowledge of many people, organize it, and present it to you in a way that is satisfying, exciting, informative, and hopefully never dull. But education is a two-way street that requires study. So what if you don't care about anatomy or classification? Read it anyway. A little pain is good for the soul!

1. CLASSIFICATION

For years, cichlidophiles have classified their fish into four categories; the African, the Asian, and the American big ones and American dwarf cichlids. Some people preferred a different classification; the dwarfs, the mouthbreeders, and the big Central and South American forms, with all others not considered. Today a new and better system is needed, if only for ease of arranging them in our minds.

The scientist, however, is not concerned with any aquarium classification. His interest is in lines of evolution, and the mechanics of the formation of species through time in response to an ever changing environment, an environment not merely physical and climatic, but biological as well. Competition for food and space and adaptations to temperature changes are only part of the picture. New predators and new diseases take their toll not only of our cichlids, but of their predators and prey as well. And the pressures of this complex environment may result in animals of only distant relationship changing, through the eons, towards very similar endpoints. This is convergent evolution, and can play havoc with any scheme of classification based on looks alone. The scientist is concerned with the evidence of the fossil record, of development, of chemistry of the body, and of the hereditary material as visualized in the chromosomes. In practice, however, much of this evidence is not yet available, difficult to come by, or just not worth the effort considering the difficulty of the problem. The ichthyologist, therefore, is primarily concerned with those things that can be well-preserved, and consequently studies mostly the bones, teeth, musculature, and geographic distribution of species (zoogeography). In 1966 a group of famous ichthyologists (P. H. Greenwood, Donn Rosen, Stanley F. Weitzman, and George S. Myers) reviewed our knowledge of modern bony fishes, and presented a classification of living fishes. That classification, as it pertains to cichlids, is presented here.

Aequidens portalegrensis, with counts indicated: scales (24 rows); un-branched, spiny dorsal rays (XV); and soft, branched dorsal rays (10). From *Handbook of Tropical Aquarium Fishes*, Axelrod and Schultz. (Notation of counts is discussed on page 16.)

TELEOSTS
Division III
Superorder Acanthopterygii
Order Perciformes
Suborder Percoidei
Family Cichlidae

The cichlids are only one family in a huge order, but are distinguished by a set of characteristics. There is only one nostril on each side of the head, instead of two. The marine family Pomacentridae is quite similar, but differs from the cichlids in possessing a bony plate near the orbit (the eye socket)—a bone the cichlids lack. In most cases, the lateral line is divided into a high upper lateral line forward, and a low short lateral line toward the rear. The scales along the lateral line are usually counted in delineating species, and this divided lateral line has been 'scale-counted' in different ways by different ichthyologists, resulting in some confusion of which species

9

Tylochromis lateralis, showing a body shape roughly intermediate between that of the *Crenicichla* below and the *Cichlasoma* on the facing page.

Crenicichla

is which. Cichlids have both a spiny and soft dorsal and anal. That is to say, the forward spines of these fins are often unbranched (spiny), and the rear ones are branched (soft). Again, the terminal spines of these fins are often very short, and some workers have counted the little ones and some have ignored them. The teeth of cichlids are very variable, and often of importance at the genus level. Cichlid teeth are almost always brown at the tips. The teeth may be simple (conical), very sharp, flattened for crushing, divided (bicuspid, tricuspid), few and far between, densely crowded, and in one or more rows in one or both jaws. They may point forward, straight up and down, or backward, be long or short, extend along the sides of the jaws, or (almost always) extend into the pharynx. There may be all the same types of teeth in the jaws, or different types in the front and along the sides. The pharyngeal teeth may vary in size, shape, and distribution. The distribution of scales on the head may vary, as may the size and design of the scales. The shape of the head varies from concave to straight to convex, above

Cichlasoma severum.

Apistogramma reitzigi.

Cichlasoma severum in an indestructible (by them) setting arranged entirely of tiered stones.

The frontal protuberance exhibited by *Cyrtocara moorei* (above) is evidenced also among other cichlids.

Two differently shaped cichlids confront each other in pugnacious attitude.

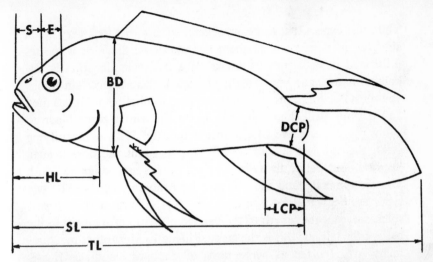

Abbreviations used on the chart are those standardly employed in recording taxonomic data and indicate measurements as follows:
S = snout length, tip of snout to edge of eye
E = eye diameter
BD = body depth at greatest dimension
HL = head length, tip of snout to rear gill cover
SL = standard length, tip of snout to base of tail
TL = total length
LCP = length of caudal peduncle, rear base of anal fin to root of tail
DCP = depth of caudal peduncle across narrowest vertical plane

and below, with or without indentations in the profile. The body may be pike-shaped, bass-shaped, or disc-shaped, or bizarre as in the angel fishes. The variation in shape is matched by extraordinary variation in markings and colors, and just leafing through this booklet will give you an idea of the variation in this large family. Behavior is important in speciation, and may also be of value in classification. Susceptibility to disease may be an indication of closeness of relationship. Indeed, many birds have been classified as distinct species on the basis of their parasites! In my own field, marine parasitology, tapeworms may prove to be the tool for separating what appear to be almost identical species of sharks and rays.

What has classification got to do with the aquarist? You and I know that we are never satisfied with even the generic identification of our fish; we want to know the exact species. This can only be done by a careful examination of the number of rays in the fins, and the scale counts, at the very least. Pictures are a naive approach.

You must expect that there are several species that look very much alike, even if only one of them has made the grade as a species illustrated in aquarium textbooks. If a fish's identification is unknown to you, and you want it identified, there are certain things you must do. First, preserve it in rubbing alcohol before it has died and decomposed. The belly should be slit with a razor blade to allow the preservative to get inside quickly. With a magnifying glass, the aquarist should do his best to count the dorsal, anal, pectoral, and pelvic fin rays. The spiny rays are designated with Roman numerals, and the soft rays by Arabic numerals. The two types are separated by a stroke, e.g., XII/9. With a clear plastic ruler, measure the length of the fish from the tip of the nose to the base of the tail fin; this is the standard length. Most other measurements are reported as percentages of standard length, as this is usually rather constant within a species over a range of sizes. You must give the standard length, however, because some species illustrate changes in the percentages with increasing size. The snout length is the distance from the tip of the nose to the front edge of the eye. The head length is the distance from the tip of the snout to the rear edge of the head, as measured by the edge of the gill cover. The peduncle length is measured from the rear of the anal fin to the base of the tail fin. Some other measureable characteristics are more difficult to do with a ruler. But if you've gone this far you have made a legitimate effort. If you cannot identify the fish on the basis of this work, you can now send it off to an ichthyologist, together with a letter stating your measurements, your source of the fish, and its coloration in life. Wrap it in a rag soaked in alcohol, place it in a plastic bag, and send it to an ichthyologist you know of. If you do know what you have, and also feel that it is rare, then you should send it to the American Cichlid Association Museum, c/o the Biology Department, Emory University, Atlanta, Georgia 30322 (att: Dr. R. J. Goldstein). Unusually valuable fishes will then be forwarded to ichthyologists concerned with the particular genus.

Further details of the anatomical variation within the family Cichlidae will be given under the entry for each genus covered in depth. Of course, all the genera cannot be covered. The reason will become obvious by looking at a list of cichlid genera, compiled by the man who organized the American Cichlid Association, Richard F. Stratton, and published in the ACA newsletter. See Table 1.

A highly developed veil angel showing hyper-attenuation of the fins.

TABLE 1
List of cichlid genera as compiled by Stratton, amended*

Acarichthys	Eretmodus	Neotilapia
Acaronia	Erythrichthys	Ophthalmotilapia
Aequidens	Etroplus	Orthochromis
Amphilophus	Genyochromis	Otopharynx
Apistogramma	Geophagus	Oxylapia
Asprotilapia	Gephyrochromis	Paracara
Astatheros	Gobiocichla	Parachromis
Astatochromis	Grammatotria	Parapetenia
Astatoreochromis	Gymnogeophagus	Paratilapia
Astatotilapia	Haligenes	Paretroplus
Astronotus	Haplochromis	Pelmatochromis
Aulonocara	Haplotaxodon	Perissodus
Aulonocranus	Hemibates	Petenia
Baiodon	Hemichromis	Petrochromis
Bathybates	Hemihaplochromis	Petrotilapia
Batrachops	Hemitilapia	Plataxoides
Bayonia	Herotilapia	Platytaeniodus
Biotodoma	Heterochromis	Plecodus
Biotoecus	Heterogramma	Pseudetroplus
Boggiania	Heterotilapia	Pseudopercis
Boulengerochromis	Hoplarchus	Pseudoplesiops
Callochromis	Hoplotilapia	Pseudotropheus
Cardiopharynx	Hygrogonus	Pterophyllum
Chaetobranchopsis	Hypsophrys	Ptychochromis
Chaetobranchus	Julidochromis	Ptychochromoides
Chaetolabrus	Labeotropheus	Retroculus
Chaetostoma	Labidochromis	Rhamphochromis
Chilochromis	Labrochromis	Saraca
Chilotilapia	Lamprologus	Sargochromis
Chromichthys	Lepidolamprologus	Sarotherodon
Chromidotilapia	Leptochromis	Satanoperca
Cichla	Leptotilapia	Schubotzia
Cichlasoma	Lestradea	Serranochromis
Cichlaurus	Lethrinops	Simochromis
Clinodon	Limnochromis	Spathodus
Cnestrostoma	Limnotilapia	Stappersia
Coptodon	Lipochromis	Steatocranus
Corematodus	Lobochilotes	Symphysodon
Crenicara	Macropleurodus	Tanganicodus
Crenicichla	Melanochromis	Teleogramma
Cunningtonia	Melanogenes	Telmatochromis
Cyathochromis	Mesonauta	Theraps
Cyathopharynx	Mesops	Tilapia
Cynotilapia	Microgaster	Tomocichla
Cyphotilapia	Mylochromis	Trematocara
Cyrtocara	Nandopsis	Tropheus
Dicrossus	Nannacara	Tylochromis
Docimodus	Nannochromis	Uaru
Ectodus	Neetroplus	Xenochromis
Enantiopus	Neochromis	Xenotilapia

* Doubtlessly, some of these names will now be considered junior synonyms and thereby invalid, and other names will have been left out.

2. BEHAVIOR

Cichlids are interesting fishes to watch. The reason, obviously, is because they behave in ways surprisingly familiar and understandable to us. One problem in describing cichlid behavior, however, is that it is considered almost sinful among biologists to ascribe human-type emotions or rational behavior to a lower animal. Instead, biologists tend to look for physical or chemical stimuli to explain such behavior. But can't the same thing be said of people?

Cichlids, as psychologists have long known, can learn. Fry may learn to follow a parent and enter a hole (especially in cave brooders and mouthbrooders). Adults learn to recognize a mate. Your fish

Impossible as it may appear, all of these *Tilapia mossambica* fry can find refuge in the parental mouth.

With fins spread and gill covers flared, this male *Cichlasoma meeki* is belligerently ready to defend against entry into his territory.

learn to recognize you when you approach the aquarium with food, whereas strangers frequently will elicit no such response. This is not to belittle the work of seeking physical and chemical stimuli for almost all aspects of behavior. What I am leading to is my reason for explaining and/or describing cichlid behavior in terms acceptable to aquarists. If we can overlook the technical explanations when speaking of human behavior, then I feel it is legitimate to do the same when describing the behavior of these very intelligent fishes. And so my biologist colleagues must forgive me when I speak of "the excited male looking for the female and being angered by the sight of a rival in his territory." And my psychologist friends must also forgive me if I prefer to ignore the words (but not the concepts) of their discipline, such as agonistic, Pavlovian, reinforcement, releasers, etc.

The study of behavior is called *ethology*. What we usually refer to as instinct may be considered the predicted behavior of a species under certain conditions. Certainly, much of this is inherited, but some of the behavior is learned, sometimes from parents, and sometimes by trial and error. Some fishes can be fooled by raising them with fishes of other species. Later in life they may not recognize their own species. Fishes are also adaptable. In the absence of a suitable mate of their own species, they may mate with a fish of another species. Some behavioral sequences, once started, cannot be turned off. In cichlids, this often translates into the situation wherein you find fish getting ready to spawn in a pet shop. You buy them, take them home and place them in very different water and lighting conditions, and they go ahead and finish what they started. Again, fishes may be frightened by bright lights or sudden movements, but when spawning they are often oblivious to these usually objectionable stimuli.

Many cichlids are pugnacious. The pugnacity is usually rooted in their territoriality. A dwarf cichlid from Central America may take over a square foot area in a corner of the aquarium. Another of the same species may take the other corner, and woe unto him who ventures into the staked-out backyard. But suppose there is less

Nannacara anomala mates poise defensively watchful over their chosen spawning site.

Aequidens pulcher pairs lock jaws in prenuptial tests of strength before accepting one another as spawning partners.

Aequidens pulcher makes no distinction in respect to size of intruders and rushes to attack the intruding finger.

than two square feet of territory? Cichlids will adjust. They will threaten each other by erecting their spiny fins and expanding their gill covers to make them look larger, and they may even resort to chasing and biting their adversaries. But they will adapt.

Work with *Nannacara anomala* has shown that the adversaries will eventually settle for a slightly smaller territory, even though they defend the boundaries vigorously. Add a third fish to the tank, keeping the space constant, and they may accept even smaller territories after the usual hassling over who gets how much. Eventually, one can add enough fish to limited space to destroy their will to defend a territory.* They are just too tired to keep up the work, and there is no point in defending a territory that's just too small to bother with. This often happens in aquarium shops. A large number of cichlids in one tank in the store seem to get along fine. But take a half dozen home to put in a 20 gallon tank, and before you know it they are fighting over the best rocks and corners. *Leptotilapia tinanti* is a bottom-skipping cichlid from Africa. The whole bottom of the tank is his territory, and he'll snap his shovel-like mouth at any fish who happens to be wherever he himself happens to be. Many fish are uninterested in maintaining territories except at spawning time. Angels are a good example of this. Also at spawning time, pairs will share a territory that previously belonged to only one of them. And there may be a change in ownership of the property. The male may stake out the territory, allow the female to enter for spawning, and then be chased out by the female who will then brood the eggs and fry. In the Lake Malawi (East Africa) 'mbuna' group of mouthbrooders, the male defends a territory until a sexually ready female comes along. Both protect the territory during the short spawning period, and then she is chased away from the territory—seduced and abandoned! Perhaps this is why the mbuna are so popular among male aquarists today. Perhaps we identify with the male mbuna. And perhaps psychologists should turn away from the tanks and look at the fishkeepers!

Fish have signals that their own species recognize, and that other species recognize. These signals may be dark markings, bright colors, erection of fins, or other acts of behavior. Many male cichlids

---

* Exceptions are *Aequidens curviceps* and *Cichlasoma nigrofasciatum*.

threaten rivals by slowly arching their bodies back and forth, as though they were beating their tails against the enemy. On the other hand, they may carry out the same motions at an eye-blurring speed, and females think this is sexy. Partners may twitch their

The fish at right in this battling pair of *Nannochromis dimidiatus* males is signalling submission in a gesture of appeasement to the winner.

heads at each other, and a similar head flick may mean something quite different to a bunch of fry watching their mother. Cichlids may lock jaws, and this usually is a means of fighting. In *Cichlasoma*, mates often do this before spawning, and perhaps this is part of the ritual of forming the pair bond. *Apistogramma reitzigi* of South America displays a myriad of patterns, and many of these have been associated with different apparent meanings. *Nannacara anomala* females develop a checkerboard pattern when brooding young of their own or even when brooding orphans. Why is it that they will brood young of different species, even different genera?

Certain colors or patterns are displayed when a territory is being defended, and this is why crowded cichlids in a shop rarely look their best under shop conditions, even when getting good food and clean water. We've already talked of threatening behavior. But how does a fish signal that he gives up? There are various ways of signaling appeasement. Some fish show their bellies to the winner. Others lower their heads. And still others change their coloration or pattern to signal 'Uncle.'

Some cichlids will fight until they can hardly be expected to recover from their wounds. Others won't fight at all. Some will vigorously defend their young, and others won't spend any effort at defense. The behavior of some mouthbrooders probably has some easily testable answer. Some won't eat at all while brooding, while others will put the eggs down somewhere reasonably safe, catch a quick lunch, and pick up the eggs again. Why do some cichlids, notably discus, suddenly go on hunger strikes, perhaps never again to eat until they die? Yet others suddenly change their minds and go back to eating. Disease or behavior? These are only some of the myriad activities one may expect to see among even the common aquarium cichlids. And among non-aquarium species, there are even more interesting, if not bizarre, kinds of activity. There are cichlids that mimic other cichlids, sneak into a school of these others, and bite them to get food. Some eat scales, and some eat eyes. Instinct? In nature, we tend to think of everything as instinctive. But in the aquarium, we often have second thoughts. We get to know our fish as we see them all the time, not some of the time. And attributing these activities to the catch-all, *instinct*, is just an oversimplification to the dyed-in-the-wool cichlid lover who swears by everything holy (brine shrimp, discus, undergravel filters) that *his* fish can think!

One aspect of cichlid lore deserves special comment. It has often been written that cichlids may mate for life. Nonsense! Under most community tank conditions, if a choice of mates is available, the partners may switch in subsequent matings. In non-community tanks, if one of a 'mated pair' dies, the other partner will often accept a new mate if offered. The 'mated pair' concept is a myth. What it really means is a *compatible* pair, fish that will accept each other frequently and will not fight excessively during non-spawning periods.

The aquarist has used physical stimuli to set off sequences of behavior. Raising the temperature is a commonly employed stimulus for triggering angels and discus, and works with some dwarf cichlids as well. Increasing the duration and intensity of light is another such stimulus. Some salt added to the water often triggers increased activity in Malawi cichlids, as does a major water change.

One aspect of behavior has an excellently researched biological basis. This is fright behavior under conditions of visual blockage. Suppose, in the dark, one fish is attacked by a predator and wounded. This often sets off a panic response in other nearby fish that cannot possibly see what has happened (even assuming they could understand what they could see). It is now known that the skin of the fish (many species, anyway) contains a type of cell, which in turn only secretes a substance into the water when the skin is broken. This substance is called "fright substance," and elicits a fright reaction in fish of the same species, as well as a less intense response in fishes of other related species. It only gets into the water upon one fish being wounded. It is an excellent chemical warning system for those not yet aware that danger is in the vicinity. So far, this system is known from atheriniform fishes. Perhaps it occurs in perciforms, too.

Most of the interesting cichlid behavior is associated with prenuptial play, spawning, and brooding. Because these activities vary

Majestic is the mien of the black angel, *Pterophyllum scalare*.

Tilapia heudelotii, often referred to as *T. macrocephala*, dissected to illustrate a mouthful of incubating eggs.

from group to group, they will be covered in the appropriate section on breeding cichlids.

The cichlid community tank deserves special comment. Many cichlids have the beauty and size to warrant special display aquaria of 100 gallons or more. These require special filtration systems, not as a consequence of the size of the aquaria, but of the large amounts of food consumed by these large fishes. Large cichlids will uproot if not destroy almost all aquarium plants. It is necessary, therefore, to decorate the aquarium with rocks, plastic plants, and pieces of cured wood or driftwood. Only one of each species should occupy the aquarium, else there is the danger of a pair setting up house-keeping and raising havoc. If the aquarist's primary interest is in breeding, but he still wants to display his prize fish between periods of fish production, then it is wise to set up two display aquaria in order to split the pairs. Territoriality will be at its minimum in an aquarium of single specimens of widely different species, especially if somewhat crowded.

3. CHOOSING CICHLIDS

It is always exciting to anticipate owning a magnificent pair of large cichlids, but the purchase of them is difficult for two reasons; the high cost of a good pair of known breeders, and their general unavailability. Most successful cichlid breeders purchase young stock in some quantity, raise the fish under the local water conditions (which may differ from the water their parents spawned in), and allow the fish to choose their own mates. This is very desirable for a number of reasons. To mention just a few: (1) by raising the fish yourself, you can be sure that the adult survivors are well-adapted to your water, foods, and feeding schedule; (2) the low cost of young fish enables you to purchase a large number and perhaps get several pairs; (3) you allow the fish to choose compatible partners and avoid unnecessary fights between belligerent strangers; (4) you've made maximal use of the large tank in which you are growing your stock. Only the well-to-do or the financially fanatic will spend the money on a breeding pair of discus, although the young are cheap. Young fish, in addition, are much more likely to adapt to a change in the environment, and for those that don't adapt, the financial loss is negligible. Finally, when it comes to the rare cichlids found in an importation of "mixed dwarfs," etc., only the young are found in a shop. Had the importer or dealer recognized what he had, the price might have been much higher. Many *Apistogramma* and African bottom-dwelling cichlids arrive as "mixed" or "unidentified" or misnamed species, and the price of these beauties is usually very low. Such lots of fishes are the aquarist's best source of the rare and exotic. If you know in advance what you want to breed, there is no problem in finding them in a shop, as regards the common species. But I, and many others, make it our business to visit the aquarium shop on the day the imports arrive, and we always bring along a good textbook to help us guess what the mystery fishes might be.

4. FEEDING CICHLIDS

In nature, many species of cichlids are insectivorous, predaceous, or even herbivorous. For example, many of the Lake Malawi 'mbuna' complex of mouthbrooders eat only algae in nature. But in the aquarium, almost all cichlids relish a diet of meat. Prepared flake foods are low priced, but should constitute a supplement, not the major part of the diet. The bulk of the diet should consist of a blend of meats. I use raw fish ("ocean perch") as the main ingredient, and to it add some liver (pork, beef, or chicken). One can also add fish roe, cod liver oil, old microworm culture, egg yolk, or anything else he desires. It is a good idea to add some vegetable matter, including mashed spinach, or, perhaps, some of your excess duckweed. The entire lot of food is made into a mash in the blender, frozen into cubes in an ice-cube tray, and the cubes thawed before feeding. The value of a mixture is to be found in the biochemical contributions of these various ingredients. Raw fish is the best source of proteins. Liver supplies carbohydrates and certain fat-soluble vitamins. Microworm cultures supply yeast, an excellent source of the multitudinous group of chemically unrelated B vitamins. Egg yolk supplies fat-soluble vitamins, and green leafy vegetables supply B vitamins again. It is not a good idea to use too much of any one of these additives, and it is definitely undesirable to add vitamin pills. Overdoses of vitamins can lead to just as undesirable effects as a possible deficiency, and it is rather difficult to give your fish a deficient diet. Remember that vitamins are only required in trace amounts, and a mixture of liver and fish is sufficient, if not optimal, for most species.

Many cichlid breeders are concerned with maximal growth in minimal time. This is best accomplished in two ways. One should feed the fish frequently, at least twice a day and preferably much more. Second, it is useful to leave the light on in the fish room 24 hours a day. This usually will not disturb breeders (the fish), and in some instances the long photoperiod may trigger nuptial behavior.

For more than ten years attempts to propagate *Symphysodon* species brought only frustration; success came only after the discovery that discus fry feed mainly upon parental skin secretions during the first few weeks of life.

Most cichlid fry can take newly hatched live brine shrimp as soon as they are free-swimming. This is the best food available. Microworms are also useful, especially for the smaller cichlid fry. One important caution about feeding microworms. The tank containing the fry should not have coarse gravel. Bare tanks are best, but fine sand is tolerable. The reason for this is that the fry may attempt to follow their prey into the gravel, become lost and lodged, and die in such set-ups.

If the fry are left with the parents, it is often not necessary (although it is still desirable) to feed live brine shrimp nauplii. The parents will frequently chew up the adult food into a fine mush, and spray it onto the shoal of fry.

Live foods for adult cichlids are always best, but not always available. Serious cichlid breeders will attempt to grow earthworms in boxes in the backyard, using soil, dead leaves, and stale bread as food. Baitstores supply crickets, mealworms, and live minnows. The use of minnows should be done cautiously. Some minnows carry monogenetic trematodes ('flukes') on the gills or skin. It is possible to infect some cichlids with the less host-specific parasites on such bait fishes. Feed bait fishes once, and then wait at least three weeks before using them again. If in the meantime your fish show signs of scratching themselves or expanded gill covers, discontinue the use of bait minnows from that source, and treat the tank with formalin, about four drops to the gallon.

Freeze-dried foods are usually accepted by all cichlids, but they are expensive.

5. PHYSICAL PARAMETERS

Irrespective of the quality of the water in their natural habitats, most cichlids will do quite well in water that is neutral to somewhat alkaline. It should be moderately hard (about 6–10 DH; for ppm multiply by 17.1). And it should be exceedingly clean and well-aerated. There are a number of exceptions to this general rule. (Discus do best in soft, slightly acid water, without too vigorous aeration.) Some salt is appreciated by many species; for example the cichlids from the large African lakes, and species of *Pelmato-chromis*, most of which are from coastal areas or somewhat saline pools. Heaters are, in most cases, unnecessary and carry the risk of a defective thermostat cooking your fishes. Room temperature in a house, if comfortable for you, is comfortable for your fishes. If the fish room is a garage or other unheated room, aquarium heaters should not be used; get an electric floor heater with fan drive. They will never cook fish. A very few species require somewhat elevated temperatures to induce the pre-nuptial play and start the spawning sequence. Heaters may be used in these aquaria. In fact, the only times I use aquarium heaters are for inducing spawning of some fishes where all else has failed, or I am anxious to get rid of a case of *Ichthyophthirius* ('ich') infestation of the tank.

A large tank-size to fish-size ratio is important to growing the fish, but usually not necessary for breeding pairs.

6. THE NOTEBOOK

A notebook is a rarely used, yet essential part, of every fish room, whether you're a cichlid fan or any other kind of aquarist. A simple composition book or spiral bound notebook is adequate, and the habit of using it should be cultivated. Whenever I get a good species, I begin a page with the name of the fish, the date, and my source. I also list my source's source if this is known. Any interesting behavior is made note of, as is the size of the fish when I get them, and their size at the first spawning, etc. One should list references to articles on the fish in national publications, as well as the pages in your several textbooks where these fishes are discussed. I always put down the dates of my observations, including spawning, hatching, free-swimming, maturity, etc., as well as how I handled the eggs, in what way the fish spawned (on a rock, in a flower pot, on a vertical wall, horizontal roof of a cave, etc.), how the parents behaved if left with the fry, whether I used methylene blue or acriflavine dye, and everything else which *might* be important some day. The memory is an unacceptable substitute for careful notes. If you become aware of scientific literature, these references should also be written down in the appropriate section of your notebook. The number, size, and color and shape of the eggs should be recorded, as well as the number of fish raised. Colors and patterns of the parents are interesting in themselves, and often shed light on what to expect from related species which you have, but have not yet bred.

7. CICHLIDS OF ASIA

Etroplus maculatus.

Etroplus suratensis.

As Asia is home to only two cichlids of interest, we should dispense with them at once. Both are chromides, and their data are given below.

ORANGE CHROMIDE	GREEN CHROMIDE
Etroplus maculatus (Bloch)	*Etroplus suratensis* (Bloch)
India and Ceylon	Ceylon
Fresh and brackish water	Brackish water
D. XVII–XX/8–10	D. XVIII–XIX/14–15
P. 15–16 L1. 35–37	L1. 35–40
A. XII–XV/8–9	A. XII–XIII/11

Very little is known of the green chromide as an aquarium fish, and it apparently cannot be maintained in the freshwater aquarium for long periods. It is only rarely imported.

The orange chromide has long been a favorite aquarium fish, being easy to keep and breed, and quite distinctive in shape and coloration. It has been behaviorally studied by Ward and Barlow (1967), from whom most of the following information has been taken. About a week after the pair have accepted each other, spawning takes place on a rock or in a cave. The eggs hang from threads, and both parents care for the brood, removing dead eggs and fanning the spawn. Pits are dug in the gravel in the meantime. Hatching occurs on the third day, and the wrigglers are moved to the pits for 5 or 6 days, after which they become free-swimming. The fry remain in a tight school around one or both parents, and are seen to glance off the sides of the adult fishes. During this glancing activity, the fry are feeding on mucus secreted by the parents. The number of mucus cells in the parental skin during this period has increased by about 34%. Because the parental slime provides important nutrition during the first critical week (as well as thereafter, when it is no longer critical), the largest batches are raised if the parents are allowed to keep the eggs. This is also true of the South American discus fish (*Symphysodon*), in which very few aquarists have raised any fish at all when the eggs were removed from the parents. After about three weeks, the parents lose interest in the fry, and may spawn again. The coloration and patterns of the parent fish are not consistent. Some pairs may turn very yellow when in breeding condition, the coloration reaching a peak about a week after spawning when the fry are about to become free-swimming. They signal danger by flicking their dark pelvic fins.

Orange chromides do well in alkaline water (pH 7.5–8.5), with some marine salts added, and a temperature just slightly above room temperature (about 28° C.). Much of the present aquarium stock is commercially bred in Florida ponds.

Wild *E. maculatus* have been shown to vary the water content of their tissues, as well as the content of cations and the vitamin ascorbic acid, when kept at temperatures above or below normal ones. See Parvatheswararao (1967) for details. See Ward and Barlow (1967) for additional references to behavior of *Etroplus*, and cichlids in general.

8. CICHLIDS OF AFRICA

Africa is the home of the largest number of genera of the family Cichlidae, in part a reflection of the speciation in Africa's Great Lakes, and in part due to the larger number of major river systems on that continent. Which brings us to two terms of interest; *riverine* and *lacustrine*, the latter term referring to lake-inhabiting forms. There are two enormous (in number of species) genera; *Tilapia* (of which aquarists have seen only a few, usually rather uninteresting, species), and *Haplochromis*. This will be rather surprising to old-timers who only think of *Haplochromis* in terms of the Egyptian mouthbrooder (which is now in *Hemihaplochromis*). The vividly beautiful mbuna of Lake Malawi (formerly Lake Nyasa) are all descendants of a *Haplochromis*-like ancestor. The genus *Pelmatochromis* boasts only a small number of species of aquarium interest, and this genus is primarily found in coastal waters of West Africa. The Stanley Pool, a basin of the Congo River, provides us with numerous genera of bottom-dwelling cichlids, the best known being *Nannochromis*. Also from this area come *Leptotilapia*, *Lamprologus* (and elsewhere also), and *Steatocranus*. It cannot be too strongly emphasized that aquarium knowledge of African cichlids, in terms of all the species to be found, is potential, not actual. Africa is just now opening up to the hobby, and there will be numerous new fish coming in for at least a decade, if not a generation, before the action tapers off.

Tilapia leucostica.

A portion of Lake Malawi (Nyasa).

Tilapia mariae, a species new to hobbyists; not mouthbrooders.

The genus *Tilapia*

Here is a large group of fishes from Africa which have had only limited appeal to aquarists in recent years. However, in the past at least one species (*Tilapia heudelotii**) was a very popular aquarium fish among cichlidophiles with large tanks. Today's low popularity may be due to a number of factors: (1) there are many species of *Tilapia*, and many of them are difficult to identify; (2) they are typically large fish; (3) although they are mostly mouth-brooders, making them easy to spawn, there are many far more colorful African fishes with this mode of incubation; (5) the name changes in recent years (synonymies, etc.) have been confusing to aquarists.

What can we say about the genus in general? Primarily, these are East African lacustrine species, although a number of species occur in Central Africa and along the upper Nile in the Mideast. Five species at least are bottom spawners, similar in habit to the South American cichlids; these are *Tilapia sparrmani*, *T. melanopleura*, *T. zillii*, *T. tholloni*, and *T. guinasana*. All the others are mouth-brooders. In only one species does the male carry the eggs; in all others it is the female that carries them. As you might expect, the single paternal mouthbrooder in the entire genus is the one fish that aquarists already know well: *T. heudelotii*. Is it any wonder that our thinking about these fishes is biased in the wrong direction?

---

* *T. heudelotii*, the black chinned mouthbrooder (syns: *T. macrocephala*, *T. microcephala*, and *T. dolloi*).

Some distribution data may prove helpful to the serious aquarist. Information in this section is taken from Lowe (1959), Trewavas (1966), Fishelson (1967), and Ruwet (1968), in order of importance. The northern limit of the genus seems to be Israel, in which several species occur: *T. zillii*, *T. aurea*, *T. nilotica*, and *T. galilaea*. This last species is of special interest, in that it demonstrates reproductive behavior intermediate between the typical mouthbrooders and the typical bottom spawners (or substrate spawners, or 'nesters').

In *typical* mouthbrooding courtship, the male stakes out a territory and will spawn with any willing female coming into his domain. Let it suffice here to say that each time the female passes over the bottom releasing eggs, the male passes over them spraying milt. Immediately, the female picks up the eggs in her mouth and the sequence is repeated until the end of the spawning period. In other words, she picks up the eggs about as fast as she lays them, and many times in the course of a mating. Afterward, she leaves the territory and is of no interest to the male who may now be watching

Tilapia galilaea.

out for another female to enter the territory. Any pair bond exists for the duration of mating only. In the substrate breeders, or nesters, a pair bond is formed which may last some considerable time. The eggs are deposited in the nest, and both parents guard them and the fry.

In the behaviorally aberrant *T. galilaea*, mouthbrooders (technically), a long-term pair bond forms, lasting up to two weeks. The female lays *all* her eggs without picking them up. They form a large sticky mass due to the presence of sticky threads (usually found in substrate spawner eggs, but not in mouthbrooder eggs). After about 10 to 15 minutes beyond the completion of spawning, and not before, either the male or the female or both will pick up the eggs for oral incubation. *T. galilaea* occurs further south into Africa. Deeper in Africa it is usually the female that is the first to pick up the eggs. In Israel it is usually the male that initiates picking them up.

Tilapia species are abundant in African lakes, as Table 2 illustrates. Data from Lowe (1959).

TABLE 2
Distribution of African lacustrine *Tilapia*, in part

Lake	Total Tilapia *species*	Endemic ones
Rudolf	3	0
Albert	4	0
Tanganyika	4	2
Edward	2	0
Victoria	2	2
Malawi	6	5
Rukwa	1	1
Jipe	2	2

A number of species, especially the riverine forms, are widely distributed throughout Africa, whereas certain lakes, especially Lake Malawi, are rich in *endemic* forms (species which occur there and nowhere else). A sampling of the species in the genus would include *squamipinnis, lidole, karongae, saka, shirana* (all endemic to Lake Malawi), *melanopleura;* two Lake Victoria endemics *(variabilis, esculenta);* *nilotica, leucostica, galilaea, zillii;* two Lake Tanganyika endemics *(karomo, tanganicae);* *pangani, grahami, girigan, alcalica, jipe, mossambica, hunteri, nigra, sparrmani, macrochir, tholloni, ander-*

39

Tilapia tholloni.

Tilapia melanopleura.

Tilapia mossambica.

sonii, rukwaensis, and *aurea.* A number of other names are now known to be invalid *junior synonyms* (a name applied to a fish already known under another name). These invalid names include *macrocephala, microcephala, dolloi, monodi, lemassoni, kacherbi,* and *nilotica exul.*

The occurrence of substrate breeders and mouthbrooders in the same genus is unusual (although it also occurs in *Geophagus* and *Pelmatochromis*), and Lowe has compared the two groups (omitting from consideration the two aberrant species, *heudelotii* and *galilaea*). Some major differences are as follows:

41

Tilapia philander.

Tilapia nilotica.

Tilapia zillii.

Substrate spawners

Male and female develop color and defend territory.

Both sexes make nest.

Long pre-nuptial period.

Both parents remain together and guard young.

Pair may remain together and spawn again and again, in monogamous relationship.

Parents remain with young at the spawning grounds, caring for them, feeding them.

Maternal brooders

Male only develops color and defends territory.

Male only makes 'nest.'

Very short pre-nuptial period.

Female leaves with eggs and goes elsewhere.

Male polygamous, taking several females that come to him in sequence.

Female travels to densely foliated brooding grounds, often far from spawning grounds.

Both Lowe (1959) and Ruwet (1968) consider substrate spawning as a more primitive type of behavior, in part limiting speciation. And they consider the maternal mouthbrooding habit more advanced, better adapted to fluctuating water levels in lakes (where spawning grounds might be desiccated and the offspring killed), and consistent with rapid speciation. Substrate breeder fry of many

Immature *Tilapia mariae.*

species will not follow the parents away from the nest, whereas mouthbrooder fry become imprinted by their moving mother, and will follow her away from danger. The imprinting helps them find the spawning grounds (which they have never seen) when mature. Fishelson (1967) imprinted mouthbrooder fry to a moving ball with a hole in it. The fry would follow the ball and enter the hole when frightened. Similar studies had been done by earlier workers also. The fry head for the dark, and will try to enter under the gill cover or even the black pupil of the eye!

The structure of the egg membrane of *Tilapia* has received attention recently (Dadzie, 1968). The external membrane *(zona radiata)* is very poorly developed, and there is no gelatinous covering layer, a layer found in several other fishes, and which functions in other species to anchor the egg to the bottom. It was clear that in the species studied, *Tilapia mossambica,* the absence of the sticky layer and the thinness of the zona radiata constitute structural losses which are acceptable to a mouthbrooding mode of incubation. The eggs of mouthbrooders in general are large, often opaque yellow-white, and millet-seed shaped. Not only are the eggs of mouth-brooding *Tilapia* different in their outer covering from eggs of nesters, but there are differences as well in the development of the embryo. The most exhaustive study on the development of the eggs is that of Fishelson (1966). Although the paper is in German, there is a comprehensive English summary, and a bibliography containing 124 literature references.

Technically, *Tilapia* Smith, 1840 is characterized by its pharyngeal structure, cycloid scales, an outer series of bicuspid teeth and several inner series of tricuspid teeth, although large fish may have some inner conical teeth.

Young fish often have an ocellus on the dorsal fin. The lower jaw and/or the belly may be black or red, or both or neither. All species of *Tilapia* are predominantly vegetarians, feeding on algae, larger plants, and frequently feeding in open surface waters on the diatoms and other floating algal cells. They should be given some plant material in the aquarium, and they are an excellent control on duckweed. Because of their rapid growth, large size, simple food requirements, and adaptability to many kinds of water (sometimes even marine!), they have been seeded all over the world in fish ponds and rice paddy fields, and thus are an important source of fish protein for many otherwise protein-deficient cultures. In some

Tilapia mossambica.

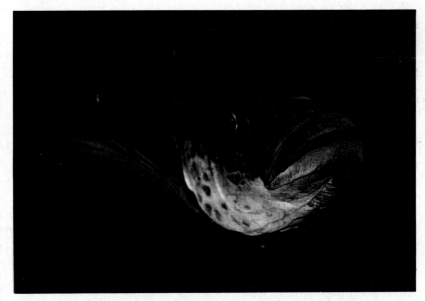

cases it has been found that the fish become so successful that they quickly reach breeding age, overpopulate the area, and become stunted from crowding, thus reducing their usefulness as food. To offset this, males of one species are stocked with females of another species. They cannot overpopulate an area as the hybrids are sterile. Paul Loiselle, whom the American Cichlid Association refers to as "Our Man in Africa," is currently involved in this work in Togo. He reports the production of a beautiful hybrid which develops a rich golden color. Unfortunately, it is sterile and thus has no future as an aquarium fish (although this is fortunate for the people it may feed). For counts of the various species, refer to any comprehensive aquarium text, e.g., Sterba (1959), or the papers cited in the Bibliography. A neglected genus, but excellent for outdoor fish ponds or large aquaria.

Tilapia heudelotii.

Tilapia guineensis.

The genus *Hemichromis*

Hemichromis Peters, 1857 is a very small genus containing only two species. These are *H. bimaculatus* Gill, 1862 and *H. fasciatus* Peters, 1857. The first species is easily recognized; this is the African jewel fish, long known to the hobby, easily kept, and easily bred. The second species, sometimes referred to as the five spot or banded cichlid, is frequently available, and yet very poorly known. There are a number of reasons for this. First, the species is widely distributed in Africa, from far West Africa eastward to the Congo and Niger Rivers, and thence southward to about Southwest Africa. When a species ranges this widely, it is expected to vary considerably in colors and sometimes in morphological characters as well, and this is the case with *H. fasciatus*. Second, aquarium stock has been confused with 'both' *Pelmatochromis arnoldi* and *P. annectens**. Paul Loiselle has deposited specimens of *H. fasciatus* in the ACA fish collection, and these are easily distinguished from my own specimens of *P. ansorgii*, even without microscopic examination. The genus *Hemichromis* is distinguished by an enlarged center pair of teeth in the jaw. This can be seen with a simple magnifying glass.

Breeding the jewel fish requires no great effort. The fish generally spawn at about $2\frac{1}{2}$ inches on a hard substrate and are excellent parents. A family of jewels is a striking sight, but the fish are some-

---

* Both "species" are the same, and the valid name is *P. ansorgii*.

47

Hemichromis fasciatus. This is the type A form, common in lagoons and large rivers and attaining a length of 18 inches.

Juvenile *Hemichromis fasciatus.* This is the type A form.

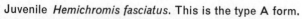

The normal rosy color of *Hemichromis bimaculatus* changes to a brilliant fiery red near spawning time; here a gently rounded rock has been chosen as the site for deposit of the eggs.

what rough (aggressive). A large aquarium containing numerous adults of rough species suits them just fine as a potential nursery, and they will spawn here as well as in their own private (not less than ten gallon) aquarium. In spawning condition, the male is a rich dark green and the female tends to reddish orange. Both are covered with iridescent scales. This coloration is variable, however, in keeping with the considerable range of this species also. It is common throughout West, Central and North Africa. Adults seldom exceed four inches in aquaria.

Hemichromis fasciatus often appears in shops at a trusting size of about an inch, under the pseudonym Lake Tanganyika cichlid. Of course, it doesn't occur anywhere near that part of Africa, and the name is totally erroneous. These young fish are often ragged and low in price. They grow quickly and don't seem to stop! An aquarium length of six inches is common, and they get much larger in nature. Spawning occurs at about five inches. The pair are excellent parents and will continue protecting very young free-swimming fry while you empty out half the water and carry the tank to a show. Mrs. Patricia Walker of Texas had this very experience and her magnificent pair of fish with their myriad fry stole the show! You just can't disturb them sufficiently to make them turn on their fry. The behavior of a number of them, not breeding, is quite another story. These fish are very vicious toward their own species, and death is a common result of their infraspecific activities. This applies to young fish as well as adults. Spawning is typically substrate breeder. The eggs are laid on a hard surface in a careful pattern, tending to concentric circles. There is no justification for removing the eggs for artificial hatching; the parents will do better than the aquarist. Counts are given below, although the fish are so different that they should not be necessary.

H. fasciatus	*H. bimaculatus*
D. XIII–XV/11–13	D. XIII–XV/9–13
A. III/8–10	A. III/7–9
Ll. 29–32	Ll. 25–29
Tr. 3–3½/10–11	Tr. 2–3/9–11

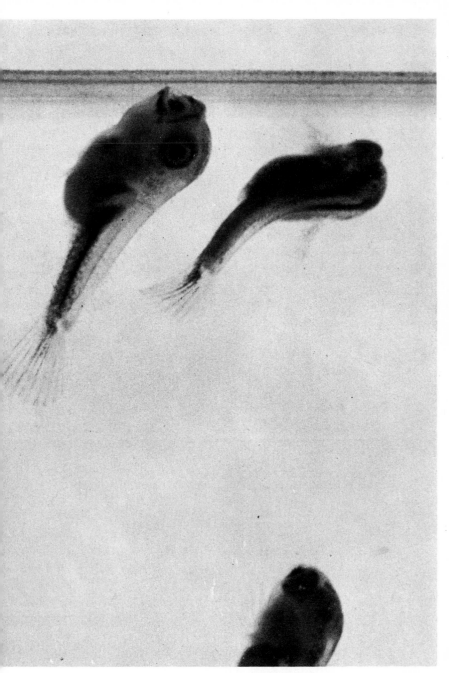

Hemichromis bimaculatus fry with yolk-sacs almost absorbed.

Pelmatochromis ansorgii, erroneously called *P. annectens*.

Female *Pelmatochromis ansorgii* (commonly called *P. annectens*), displaying silvery scales **above** the vent.

Overhead placement of the eggs of *Pelmatochromis ansorgii*.

Hemichromis fasciatus, juvenile of type **B**

The jewel fish is recommended for every cichlid enthusiast. But the five spot is not recommended for anyone but the most dedicated cichlidophile with a large tank to spare. Both species are prolific, usually more so than the aquarist would wish, and many young will probably have to be given away or destroyed.

The genus *Pelmatochromis*

The genus *Pelmatochromis* consists of about 25 species of rather dissimilar West African fishes. The approximate range of the genus is from Senegal to the Congo, with one species reported from Lake Rudolf in Kenya (East Africa). Most of the aquarium species are coastal forms, occurring in fresh to highly saline water, and some salt in their aquaria may be to their liking. The definitive characteristic shared by these fishes is the presence of a large, rather fleshy, rough-surfaced pad medial to the top of the gill arches. A similar character (and this is certainly an unusual character!) occurs in one

Pelmatochromis taeniatus.

Pelmatochromis ansorgii.

Spawning *Pelmatochromis thomasi.*

Pelmatochromis kingsleyae.

Pelmatochromis pulcher, the *"P. kribensis"* of the aquarium trade.

Pelmatochromis humilis.

East African genus also, but it is not so well developed as in *Pelmatochromis*. The variation in breeding styles is considerable. At least one species, *P. guentheri*, is a mouthbrooder. Most of the well-known species are cave-spawners. Some appear to be open-area spawners, but it may be that in nature they prefer very large rock caves and will not accept small flowerpots; hence we tend not to think of them as cave-spawners in the usual aquarist's sense.

Aquarists have long used the following names for their species of *Pelmatochromis*: *P. kribensis, P. subocellatus, P. taeniatus, P. pulcher, P. arnoldi* and *P. annectens* to name a few. It now appears that most of these names are either invalid or wrongly applied. Recently, D. Thys van den Audenaerde (1968) published a preliminary revision of the entire genus, indicating the existence of previously unknown species, and calling attention to the situation wherein aquarists have used incorrect names for many years. His analysis follows.

TABLE 3
The genus *Pelmatochromis* according to Thys, 1968

Subgenus *Pelmatochromis*

1. *P. buettikoferi* (Steindachner, 1894): Liberia, perhaps Sierra Leone.
2. *P. corbali* (Boulenger, 1913): Portuguese Guinea, Senegal.

Subgenus *Chromidotilapia*

3. *P. guentheri* (Sauvage, 1882): Sierra Leone to Southern Cameroon. Synonyms: *P. pellegrini*, *P. boulengeri*, *Hemichromis voltae*, *H. tersquamatus*.
4. *P. kingsleyae* (Boulenger, 1898): Gabon. Synonyms: *P. haugi*, *P. regani*.
5. *P. batesii* Boulenger, 1901: Rio Muni, Fernando Po, Southwest Cameroon.
6. *P. loennbergi* Trewavas, 1962: Western Cameroon.
7. A new species, not yet named: Congo and Gabon, known in the literature under various incorrect names.
8. *P. schoutedeni* Poll and Thys, 1967: Congo.
9. *P. exsul* Trewavas, 1933: Kenya (Lake Rudolf). (This is rather eastern!)

Subgenus *Pelvicachromis*

10. *P. humilis* Boulenger, 1916: Sierra Leone, Guinea.
11. *P. pulcher* Boulenger, 1901: Nigeria. Often confused in aquarium literature with *P. kribensis*. Synonym: *P. aureocephalus*.
12. *P. cf. pulcher:* Southern Nigeria, Cameroon. Syn.: *P. camerunensis*. (This is probably the fish which American aquarists call *P. pulcher*, and which was discussed by Heiligenberg, 1965b).
13. *P. roloffi* Thys, 1968: Sierra Leone, Guinea, and perhaps Liberia.
14. *P. taeniatus* Boulenger, 1901: Nigeria and Cameroon. Synonyms: *P. kribensis*, *P. kribensis* var. *calliptera*, *P. klugei*, *P. kribensis klugei*.
15. *P. subocellatus* (Günther, 1871): Gabon to Congo.
16. *P. cf. subocellatus:* Southern Nigeria.
17. *P. longirostris* Boulenger, 1903: Cameroon, Gabon, Rio Muni.
18. *P. species:* Ghana.
19. *P. caudifasciatus* Boulenger, 1913: Cameroon, Gabon, Rio Muni.
20. *P. sp.:* Sierra Leone (see Proc. USNM *92*: 301).
21. *P. cf. caudifasciatus:* Central Congo and Ogowe River system. Originally called *Nannochromis squamiceps* by Boulenger, 1902.

Tilapia-like Group

22. *P. ruweti* Poll and Thys, 1965: Angola to Katanga in the Congo.
23. *P. ocellifer* Boulenger, 1899: Gabon, Congo. Synonyms: *Paratilapia nigrofasciata*, *P. dorsalis*, *P. longipinnis*.
24. *P. congicus* Boulenger, 1897: Congo.

Miscellaneous species

25. *P. ansorgii* Boulenger, 1901: Nigeria, Ghana. Synonyms: *P. arnoldi*, *P. annectens*, *P. maculifer*, *Tilapia maculifer*.
26. *P. cerasogaster* (Boulenger, 1899): Congo.
27. *P. thomasi* (Boulenger, 1915): Sierra Leone, Guinea, Liberia.

Spawning *Pelmatochromis pulcher*.

Pelmatochromis buettikoferi.

Pelmatochromis guentheri.

Refer to the captions to the photographs for identifications. The major revisions, as concerns the hobby, are that: (1) *P. kribensis* is no longer valid, and the name is now *P. taeniatus*. Neither is *P. klugei* valid. Thus, *P. taeniatus* is the only valid name in the so-called *taeniatus-klugei-kribensis* group. (2) We no longer have to distinguish between *P. annectens* and *P. arnoldi*. The valid name for both 'species' is now *P. ansorgii*. (3) The fish that we have been calling *P. pulcher* is closely related to, but not identical to, that species, and has no name for now. (4) The real *P. pulcher* has often been illustrated in hobby publications under the name *P. kribensis* (see Axelrod and Schultz, *Handbook of Tropical Aquarium Fishes*, p. 646). In short, the aquarium *taeniatus* is correctly named, and *kribensis* is an invalid name for the same fish. The aquarium '*kribensis*' is really *pulcher*. And the aquarium *pulcher* is an unnamed species.

To my knowledge, this information first was brought to the attention of the aquarium hobby by Terofal, writing in the April, 1969 issue of DATZ.

It will take a long time for these changes to work their way into aquarium usage, and in the meantime it may be that Thys' scheme will not be accepted. But we must assume that the work is valid, and there is no time like the present for getting used to using these new names.

A comprehensive description of the behavior of the mouthbrooding species, *P. guentheri*, was given by Myrberg (1965). Color variation of what seems to be *P. cf. pulcher* (or *P. camerunensis* of European aquarists) was described by Heiligenberg (1965b).

The following information is summarized from Myrberg (1965). In this species *(P. guentheri)* it is the female that holds a territory, spawning with males entering the territory. There is the usual courtship and pair bond formation found in the substrate breeders. At the end of this time, spawning occurs. And now mouthbrooding comes into play, but instead of the female picking up the eggs for oral incubation, it is the male that is the brooder. The fish remain together. After 9 to 12 days the young are released and defended by both parents. At night, or in periods of danger, both parents will pick up the young in their mouths for up to 10 to 12 days from original release time. After this time the young are too large to protect orally, but the parents will defend them anyway for 30 to 40 days post-release.

Myrberg came to a number of conclusions on the basis of his extensive studies with this species. First, the pair bond is rather strong, about as strong as in most substrate breeders, and this applies to other specialized mouthbrooders such as *T. heudelotii, Geophagus jurupari*, and the unusual *T. galilaea* (see previous section on *Tilapia*). Second, both *P. guentheri* and the South American *G. jurupari* spawn on a large, solid object, not in a sand depression as do most of the maternal brooders. Third, the pair prepare the spawning site, as in the two *Tilapia* and the *Geophagus* species cited above. This is in contrast to most maternal brooders, where the male alone prepares the site. Fourth, egg pickup occurs when spawning is just about over (approximately 40 minutes after it begins). Recall that in *T. galilaea* an interval of about 10 or 15 minutes post-spawning must elapse. In *Geophagus jurupari* the delay is about 24 hours. In most of the maternal mouthbrooders, eggs are picked up during spawning or immediately afterward. Fifth, the duration of parental care is similar to that of most substrate breeders, and very much longer than most maternal mouthbrooders. Sixth, the fact that the male alone incubates the eggs resembles the situation in *T. heudelotii*. Many additional observations and conclusions

Pelmatochromis guentheri.

Pelmatochromis pulcher, formerly identified under one of its synonyms as *P. aureocephalus*.

Pelmatochromis taeniatus, formerly called **P. klugei.**

Pelmatochromis ocellifer.

were made, but we cannot cover them all here. Paul Loiselle writes (pers. comm.) that *P. guentheri* behaves in nature in the same way that it behaved in Myrberg's aquaria. And that is proof of good experimental design.

The cave-spawning species of *Pelmatochromis* are generally strikingly beautiful fishes. I will discuss *P. pulcher* and *P. cf. pulcher*. Both spawn in deep caves constructed under large rooted plants or rocks, or in ready-made rock caves. The caves must be rather deep and hidden from much light. In my experience *P. pulcher* spawns on a vertical wall of the cave, whereas *P. cf. pulcher* prefers the roof. These observations are based on numerous spawnings, but very few pairs, and thus may be pair-specific (and meaningless) rather than species-specific. The eggs of both are large, ovoid, tan, with a light pole distal and a dark short thread proximal by which they are loosely anchored to the rock. Most writers will agree with me that the parents are not reliable and may eat the eggs. There is a very long period of pre-nuptial display by the female prior to spawning, and the aquarist may be exasperated waiting for the big event to happen the first time.

When the actual spawning finally occurs (if it is not observed, one may check the cave, if it is constructed properly, with a flashlight) the cave should be dismantled and the rock containing the eggs removed. A gallon jar containing filtered water from the aquarium is set on a table in a warm room, and enough methylene blue added to darken the water *until you can barely see your hand behind it*. Too little dye is worthless. The dye is harmless to the eggs and fry even in great concentrations. The rock is positioned so that the eggs hang downward. A gentle stream of air is played next to, but not on, the egg patch. The jar is protected from light by inserting it inside a shopping bag or facsimile. Warmth, darkness, methylene blue, and gentle aeration are all that are required. The eggs should be checked daily, and fungused or whitened ones squirted off with an eyedropper. If the fungus patch is excessive, squirt everything off the rock allowing the eggs to remain on the bottom, and removing the dead and contaminated material. Methylene blue in weak concentrations will retard the growth of some kinds of bacteria but not others. In high concentrations it will affect more species of bacteria, perhaps all species that might damage incubating eggs under normal aquarium conditions. The mode of action of the dye remains unknown to this day, but it *has* been shown to act in *electron transport*, the process that describes respiration. Its activity in electron transport has not been experimentally related to how it acts on bacteria.

The eggs hatch in about 3 days and fall to the bottom *(pulcher)* or remain stuck to the rock *(cf. pulcher)*. At 5 to 8 days the fry are mostly sliding around on the bottom in an upright position, and the next day they are free-swimming, and behaving as a shoal. The fry should now be poured into a half-filled 10 gallon aquarium for growth. Food should consist of microworms and newly-hatched brine shrimp. A source of plant food should be available, and hair algae is excellent for this purpose. Maintain warm temperatures constantly. Growth is dependent on the feeding schedule and the room. In my experience, *cf. pulcher* reaches an inch in 3 months; *P. pulcher* reaches a half inch in a month. Growth is thereby neither very slow nor fast, and it must be kept in mind that *P. cf. pulcher* is a larger adult fish than is *P. pulcher* (the aquarium *'kribensis'*).

Heiligenberg (1965b) reported an unusual phenomenon in the genus *Pelmatochromis*, and assumed that aquarists were familiar with it. I certainly wasn't! But he seems to have hit on something definite and very odd. When the fish are bred in acid water (pH 4–5), there may be 90% males; at neutral pH, there may be 90% females. It is therefore suggested that species of *Pelmatochromis* be bred at *varying* pH values, to assure enough of both sexes to make distribution of the stock easy. The sex determining mechanism remains unknown.

Pelmatochromis cf. pulcher also exhibits two types of males (at least), some with the red region restricted to the belly (as in *P. pulcher*) and some with the red region extending from the belly all the way to the snout. Both are found living in the same waters in West Africa, and so this is not a subspecific difference (which requires geographical separation). *P. cf. pulcher* is a darker fish than *P. pulcher*, but this cannot be judged if the fish are on a dark background; the 'kribs' will darken too much for you to be sure. The species differ in size and in rows of teeth.

Pelmatochromis ansorgii has never been popular, in part because it is not especially pretty, and in part because it is difficult to identify. Young fish are found in commercial imports from Africa,

A rather yellowish variety of *Pelmatochromis pulcher*, referred to as *P. aureocephalus* in the hobby.

Pelmatochromis taeniatus.

often rather nondescript and variable in their dark markings. Some have horizontal bands (common in the genus but not seen in adults of this species), but most have a series of six dark large blotches along the body at the midline, and one may see another series of smaller, less distinct blotches immediately above. Adults show all these blotches distinctly. In my strain, the base of the dorsal of the female has a series of fine dark spots, but the male does not; the tail fin of the male is asymmetrical, the upper lobe being longer than the lower. The unpaired fins of both sexes have dust fine speckling tending to a reticulation.

Courtship and sexual coloration is practically undeveloped. Behaviorally, these fish are mediocre at best. There are reports of the female developing a pretty red coloration near the belly, but mine did not develop it. The females, when in good health and mature, have a group of silvery white scales above the vent. It does not indicate imminent spawning, only a mature healthy female. Spawning is usually a surprise to the aquarist. The fish will spawn in a cave, out in the open, or in a flowerpot. Eggs resemble those of the previously discussed species, but are somewhat smaller. The fish are poor parents, and the eggs should be removed, and handled as before.

A high temperature triggers the spawning sequence, but may result in deformed fry. I recommend raising the temperature to about 82° F. to induce spawning, but holding the eggs at room temperature.

The species is native to the lower Niger River of Nigeria, and elsewhere into Southwestern Ghana.

Congo River Cichlids

In recent years, a number of bottom-dwelling cichlids have been imported from the Congo, that huge river that drains the entire country of the same name. Many subsidiary rivers empty into this massive stream, which finally reaches the Atlantic well below the equator at the border of Congo and Angola. It is certain that only an extremely small percentage of its cichlids has yet been seen by the hobby. As these are all bottom-dwellers, it is likely that they come from areas of rapids, much like our own native darters (*Etheostoma* and others).

Nannochromis nudiceps.

The first and most popular to come in was *Nannochromis nudiceps.* They are found near Kinshasa where the Congo spreads out into a lake (the Stanley Pool) before resuming its now short course to the sea. The coloration of *N. nudiceps* is magnificent, primarily light blue with iridescent green highlights at the front. The female is the more colorful of the two. Many people wonder why their nudiceps don't spawn when they always look as though they are about to. The answer is simply that they are not in proper condition. In this species, it is normal for the ovipositor to be partly extruded. It does not indicate imminent spawning. Before spawning, the female becomes enormously distended. As fat as a house is rather descriptive. Under these conditions, there is no way to turn them off. If you find them this fat in your local shop, buy them, for they will no doubt spawn within a couple of weeks.

Breeding takes place preferably in a cave, and the deeper the better. But they will spawn in a small flowerpot if they are ready and nothing else is available. The eggs are large, ovoid, opaque, white,

Teleogramma species.

Nannochromis nudiceps.

Many of the new (and as yet unidentified) cichlids from the Congo River are bottom dwellers possessing only vestigial swim bladders. They are mostly very plain fishes, with little difference in the appearance of male and female in each species. Although there have been no reports of the spawning behavior of Congo River bottom species like the two shown here, there is a great probability that the fishes are not mouthbrooders and that both parents guard the eggs.

and hang loosely from very short threads. Both parents defend the eggs and young. I have not succeeded in artificially hatching the eggs (as done with most substrate breeders), but it probably can be done. For a successful breeding, see the report by Richter (1969) in T.F.H. magazine. *Nannochromis dimidiatus* has been recently imported in quantity. It is hoped that this red and orange beauty will lend itself to propagation. A very peaceful fish, which grubs in gravel.

Below, a portion of the Stanley Pool near Kinshasha; opposite, lower photo: a view of the Congo River a few miles east of Kinshasha.

Nannochromis dimidiatus.

Teleogramma brichardi.

Leptotilapia (formerly *Gobiochromis*) *tinanti.*

Both sexes of young *Steatocranus casuarius* develop a cranial protuberance, but the protuberance is more prominent in the male (upper fish in the photo above) and becomes accentuated in older males (below).

Lamprologus werneri.

Also from the Stanley Pool vicinity comes the shovelmouth cichlid, *Leptotilapia tinanti*. This drab-colored bottom hopper has a maw suited to moving lots of gravel (which it doesn't do), and an almost human expression to its face. Its territory includes the whole bottom of the tank, wherever it happens to be. It will chase any and all fishes away, and that cavernous mouth would scare anything. It is difficult to keep two in the same tank, unless the tank is kept covered and there are plenty of rocks for hiding places. One of the two is often chased right out of the tank! The shovelmouth often comes in mixed shipments with *nudiceps* and the vicious *Lamprologus mocquardi*. Another *Leptotilapia** is coming in regularly (see below).

Lamprologus mocquardi looks like a washed out *nudiceps*, but can be recognized by a red-black iridescent spot on the gill cover, and dark fuzzy markings over the body. A very nasty customer. Apparently neither of these two species has yet been reported as bred (in the American literature). This may be the same as *L. congolensis.*

---

* *Leptotilapia:* a junior synonym used in aquarium texts is *Gobiochromis.*

A very peaceful, if shy, species from this same region is the lumphead or lionhead, *Steatocranus casuarius*. This fish achieves a rather healthy size (about five inches) in the aquarium, and the older and bigger it gets, the larger becomes the fleshy forehead *(frontal gibbosity)*. It is a brownish fish, not pretty by any means, but its gentleness and ease of breeding are sure to keep it popular. They prefer to breed in a cave, and are good parents. Although the male develops a really massive lump on his head, the female develops a pretty good sized lump too. Large aquaria necessary. The young are now commonly available.

In shipments of *Steatocranus* there often occurs another species which is marked just like the lionhead. It has the brown squares to the body, and the dark mark on the dorsal fin. If one looks closely, however, it is clear that the body on this second fish is considerably longer, and it is a bottom skipper. This is another species of *Leptotilapia*. The resemblance to the lionhead even extends to its having a rather high forehead.

Another handsome genus is *Teleogramma*, worm-shaped bottom hopping cichlids which also prefer cave spawning. The large, opaque eggs are laid on the roof of the cave. The three species known to aquarists so far include *T. brichardi*, a blackish fish, *T. monogramma*, and *T. gracile*.

Lamprologus congolensis.

Cichlids of Madagascar

The Malagasy Republic occupies the entire island of Madagascar, which lies in the Indian Ocean, separated from the coast of Southeast Africa by the Mozambique Channel. A number of species and genera of cichlids are endemic to this tropical island. Recently,

Cyphotilapia (Paratilapia) frontosa from mainland Africa.

Kiener and Maugé (1966) reviewed the cichlids of the island.

The largest genus is *Paretroplus*, with five species; *P. dami, P. polyactis, P. maculatus, P. petiti*, and *P. kieneri*. These are generally deep-bodied fishes with small heads, superficially resembling *Etroplus*, or *Cichlasoma centrarchus*. *P. maculatus* has a large dark blotch above and behind the pectoral fin. *P. polyactis* has short bars along the upper part of the sides. *P. dami* has a rather enlarged snout area.

Paratilapia polleni is a darkly beautiful fish, with well developed finnage, and Jack Dempsey front profile. It is covered with light spots set in startling contrast.

Ptychochromis oligacanthus is another pretty species, which exists as different geographic races along the island. They may be dark, light, or intermediate with a series of three or four large blotches. The general coloration is blue-gray to red-brown. The dorsal may be violet, edged in dark red. The caudal and anal may be dark red. The most colorful form is from the area of Mandritsara, in the interior north of the island. The less colorful forms are coastal.

Oxylapia polli is an elongate fish with a dark blotch at the upper angle of the gill cover. It is not an attractively colored species, but its shape makes it easy to identify if you know that it's from Madagascar.

Ptychochromoides betsileanus is generally sunfish shaped, but it has a very enlarged lump on its forehead, almost (but not quite) as impressive as in the lumphead, *Steatocranus*, from the Congo. It even more closely resembles the African species, *Cyphotilapia (Paratilapia) frontosa*. Again, knowing the origin of the fish, this frontal gibbosity makes identification easy.

Tilapia melanopleura and *T. mossambica* have been introduced and established on the island.

Apparently none of these native fishes has yet been introduced to the hobby, at least in the United States. And so we have something else for cichlidophiles to look forward to. Notice the absence of *Haplochromis* and native *Tilapia* from the island.

Madagascar is a mountainous land, rising out of a 12,000 foot sea bed. Due west, from the north of the island, are the famous Comoro Islands, home of that Devonian relic, the coelacanth.

The Rift Valley System of Africa

The Great Rift Valley is discontinuous. It arises in North Africa, at the southern tip of the Arabian peninsula where the Red Sea meets the Gulf of Aden. It consists of a giant valley running down the midline of a great mountain system to its left and right. At its beginning it heads southwest in an arc with the Gulf of Aden, and then abruptly swings to a southeast arc. Far to the west it is also seen, swinging southeast and then southwest and finally straight south. Where there are two great rift valleys, at the disjuncture, a large area between is taken up by the rather shallow, yet enormous, Lake Victoria. This lake does not lie within either of the two rift valleys, but between them. You will have to examine a map to see this. It is usually the lakes along the southern part of the rift valley system that are called the Rift Lakes. The first (northernmost) Rift Valley lake is Lake Albert. It has a depth of 2,030 feet or about a half mile. From this lake we move south through the Semliki forest along the Semliki River to Lake Edward, almost 3000 feet deep. The forest and river leading to this lake are in a land called Ruwenzori, whose southern tip is on the Equator. From Lake Edward below the Equator, we continue our southward journey passing through the eastern limit of Congo to Lake Kivu with a depth of almost 4,800 feet! The eastern shore of Lake Kivu is the country Rwanda, to the south of Uganda (eastern shore for the other two lakes). Still heading south and overland, we next come to the longest of the rift lakes, Lake Tanganyika. This lake is 4,700 feet deep and covers an area of 12,700 square miles. It is bordered by The Congo to the west, Zambia to the southwest, Tanzania to the east, and Burundi to the northeast. Trekking overland to the east-southeast, we pass the relatively insignificant Lake Rukwa, and then head south where we come upon Lake Malawi (formerly Lake Nyasa). Its south and western shores are the Republic of Malawi (formerly Nyasaland), and its eastern shores are Tanzania and then Mozambique. Lake Malawi is 2,600 feet deep and occupies 11,000 square miles. South of it, lodged between Malawi and Mozambique, is Lake Chilwa. To the west of the Rift Valley Lakes are Lakes Mweru and Bangweulu. There are many other major lakes along and throughout East Africa, and they are virtually unknown to the aquarium hobby. At present, aquarists are familiar with some of the fishes of Lakes Malawi and Tanganyika, but we will discuss some

of the other lakes as well in anticipation of all the good things that are bound to come in within the next decade. Whereas the principal rift valley lakes (Albert, Edward, Kivu, Tanganyika, and Malawi) are deep clefts in the earth's crust, Lake Victoria is generally considered a saucer, only 270 feet deep, but 26,000 square miles in area!

Lake Malawi (Nyasa)

Although a very deep lake, fish life is restricted to the upper waters, where the water is oxygenated and varies from 23.5 to 27.5° C (about room temperature) all year round. The deeper waters of the lake are slightly cooler, and very low or lacking in oxygen. The inflow from rivers is insignificant, and the lake receives most of its water from rain, usually in the form of night-time prolonged violent thunderstorms. Beauchamp (1964) has described this and other rift lakes in considerable detail. Much of the surrounding region is arid. Because the land temperatures fluctuate considerably, but not the water temperature, the mornings consist of warm air

A portion of Lake Malawi (Nyasa), showing cloud-like swarms of insects hovering over the water.

Pseudotropheus auratus releasing young from mouth.

rising over the lake. This is actually visible, as these warm columns may be occupied by swarms of flies looking, as Beauchamp has said, like "bush fires several miles out on the lake."

This situation applies to the other rift lakes as well. As the warm air over the lakes rises, it creates strong winds heading out to the lakes. The African name for Lake Albert means 'destroyer of locusts,' as a consequence of the winds blowing the locusts out to the lake where they eventually fall and drown. The low temperature variation of the lakes prevents the lakes from 'turning over' annually as do the American Great Lakes. Turnover would bring up nutrients from the bottom and oxygenate the depths, but this doesn't happen in the deep rift lakes. Instead, organic material continues to fall to the bottom where it accumulates as a gray or black mud.

Our knowledge of the cichlids of this lake goes back a long way. In the nineteenth century Sir John Kirk collected fishes from Lake Malawi (then L. Nyassa or Nyasa), and these were described by

Günther (1864). Additional fishes were collected by Sir Harry Johnson, and Günther (1893) described these also. A Captain Rhodes also collected in the lake, and Boulenger (1908–1915) described these specimens. But the first significant dissertation on the cichlids of the lake was done as late as 1921 by C. Tate Regan. Regan recorded 84 species from the lake, and all except five of them were endemic, i.e., not found anywhere else. There were five species of *Tilapia* found, a number of genera containing one to three species each, and a large group of *Haplochromis* and

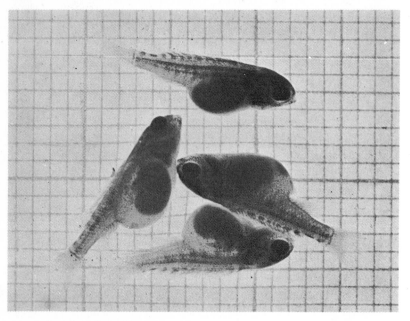

Newly hatched *Pseudotropheus* fry.

Haplochromis-like species. *Haplochromis* is a large, successful African genus, found in many waters, but this large group evidently evolved right there in the lake. For a large portion of these obviously *Haplochromis*-derivatives, he coined the genus name *Pseudotropheus*. The dentition resembled that of the Tanganyikan genus *Tropheus*, except that *Pseudotropheus* had some extra teeth, situated along the sides of the lower jaw. At this time Regan recognized at least five species, *P. williamsi*, *P. zebra*, *P. novemfasciatus*, *P. auratus*, and

Pseudotropheus zebra, male.

P. tropheops. On the other hand, he recognized 52 distinct species of *Haplochromis*, many of these (we know today) highly colored, and some considered in, or allied to, *Pseudotropheus*. Regan's fish were collected by one Rodney Wood, and deposited in the British Museum. Regan was excited about the lake, and wanted more specimens to study. At his urging, a further collection was made by Dr. Cuthbert Christy during 1925–1926. The Christy collection contained 3,500 specimens! Although Regan began work on this collection, he never finished it.

The work was taken up and completed by Dr. Ethelwynn Trewavas who published it as a synopsis of the fishes of the lake (Trewavas, 1935). She found many more species and genera. She stated, "twenty-three genera are here recognized, of which 20 are endemic and 14 are *monotypic*" (a genus containing but a single species). And, "of the 175 species comprised in these genera, 101 belong to the large genus *Haplochromis*." Greenwood (1964) assesses the situation now at 23 endemic genera and 189 endemic species. (See Table 5).

Cyrtocara moorei from Lake Malawi.

Haplochromis polystigma.

Haplochromis euchilus.

Pseudotropheus novemfasciatus, female.

Labeotropheus fuelleborni.

90

In the 1950's, Dr. Geoffrey Fryer studied the ecology of the lake, and in 1959 published his major work, emphasizing the fishes of the shoreline. His main interest was with the highly colored *Haplochromis*-derivatives of the rocky shore, which some of the natives called the 'mbuna', and which aquarists today call the 'Lake Nyasa cichlids.'

It must be emphasized that only a very few species of these very many and variable fishes have yet been seen by aquarists, and many have come in misidentified. See Table 4 for a list of the fishes studied by Fryer. How many do you recognize?

TABLE 4
Some cichlids of Lake Malawi (after Fryer)

Pseudotropheus	*Petrotilapia*	*Gephyrochromis*
novemfasciatus	*tridentiger*	*moorei*
tropheops		*lawsi*
auratus	*Cyathochromis*	
fuscus	*obliquidens*	*Labeotropheus*
fuscoides		*fuelleborni*
zebra	*Cynotilapia*	*trewavasae*
elongatus	*afra*	
minutus		*Labidochromis*
williamsi	*Melanochromis*	*coeruleus*
livingstoneii	*melanopterus*	*vellicans*
elegans	*vermivorus*	
lucerna	*brevis*	*Genyochromis*
	perspicax	*mento*
	labrosus	

Other cichlids, after additional authors*

Tilapia (4)	*Astatotilapia*	*Cyrtocara*
	calliptera	*venusta*
		annectens
		moorei
Corematodus	*Serranochromis*	*Rhamphochromis* (6)
shiranus	*thumbergii*	
Hemitilapia	*Haplochromis* (52)	*Aulonocara*
oxyrhynchus		*nyassae*
Otopharynx	*Lethrinops* (4)	
auromarginatus,		
selenurus		
Chilotilapia	*Docimodus*	
rhodesii	*johnstoni*	

* There will doubtlessly be a number of synonymies.

Haplochromis species.

Labeotropheus trewavasae.

Pseudotropheus elongatus.

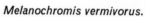

Melanochromis vermivorus.

Breeding the mbuna or *Haplochromis*-derivatives presents no difficulty. So far a number of them have been imported and bred by aquarists all around the country. Because the price of these fishes still remains in the range of twenty to seventy dollars a pair for adults, many aquarists find it wise to purchase a number of young of one species, raise them, breed them, and trade fry through the mails. One can ship a box of 60 one-inch fish, air mail, special delivery, for about six dollars, or a dozen small fry for under two dollars.

The mbuna bred so far in this country include *Pseudotropheus zebra, P. auratus, P. tropheops* (synonym: *P. macrophthalmus*), *Labeotropheus trewavasae, L. fuelleborni, Labidochromis coeruleus,* and the lavender Malawi cichlid, the specific identity of which still is a matter of contention. The only fish which seems to give aquarists trouble is *Pseudotropheus elongatus*, which has been bred, but only occasionally, and which is a rather nasty tempered (although beautiful) fish. All the others have been bred frequently and easily.

Mottled variety of *Pseudotropheus zebra.*

A *Pseudotropheus zebra* male spawns with *P. tropheops* female as puzzled catfish looks on.

The dominant male (usually the biggest) develops the best colors (except for *P. auratus*, in which almost all males show good color) and digs out a clearing in the gravel, usually down to the floor of the aquarium. When a female approaches, his colors intensify and he darts out to display to her. The display consists of swimming around her back and forth, cutting off her avenues of retreat, all the while with fins spread wide. If the female is in condition (quite fat, sometimes with a nipple where other cichlids develop a distinct spawning tube), her color will be muddy in stark contrast to the male. Spawning commences with the female brushing her vent across the 'nest' and leaping out of the way as the male does the same. Then he jumps away as she again passes her vent over the nest. While the male is fertilizing the eggs, the female is picking them up in her mouth as fast as she can. The eggs are very large, yellowish white, millet-shaped and non-sticky, and you can see them being blown around by the currents set up by the fish's activity. Often the female picks them up while they are blowing about in the water above the nest.

Melanochromis species, popularly known as the lavender Malawi cichlid.

Labidochromis coeruleus.

Melanochromis vermivorus, young female.

Aerial view of a portion of the Stanley Pool.

The entire spawning usually lasts in the neighborhood of 30 to 45 minutes or more. In *Labidochromis coeruleus*, the female may wait until spawning is completed before picking up the eggs.* In general, the excited male vibrates his body rapidly, fins erect, both prior to and during his expulsion of sperm. The female doesn't vibrate to anywhere near the same degree, if at all. At the conclusion of the spawning, the female flees the area, as the male still wants to continue. She, however, has had it and takes off for distant parts, usually among floating plants at the other end of the tank. She should now be removed to a separate tank, or the male should be removed. This depends, of course, on whether they have spawned in a private aquarium or in a community tank, and both methods are used about equally by different aquarists. There is no danger in netting out the female. She will not spit out or swallow the eggs.

The incubation period varies from three to five weeks, according to temperature and species. During this time it is not necessary to feed the female. Some will not eat at all *(P. zebra)*, some will spit

* One report by an aquarist friend.

out the eggs to eat and then pick them up again *(P. auratus)*, and some will carefully eat with the eggs still in the mouth *(lavender cichlid)*. This variation among species probably applies within species as well, so don't be surprised if your fish do it differently. It is not *necessary* to feed any of them while brooding.

Toward the end of the incubation period, the female's throat becomes blackened, as a consequence of the babies inside. In the last days, she will search out the thickest plants or mops in anticipation of the blessed event. She may release all her fry at once, or she may spit out a few a day, picking them up again at night if they still have yolk sacs. There is much variation at this stage. She develops a pattern resembling that of a male, but not nearly so intense, and this is probably a warning signal to other fishes to keep away. Eventually all the fry are out to stay, and the female should be removed. But you aren't done with her yet. She should not be placed back in the community tank in this weakened condition, but should be placed by herself in a recuperation tank and fed the very best foods. When she has regained her strength (about two weeks), she may be placed in the community tank once again. In the meantime, the fry should be fed brine shrimp in quantity and moved to larger quarters as necessary. Spawns vary from a few to fifty or more, depending on the size of the female more than anything else.

There are a few principles to keep in mind with the Malawi community tank. First, the water should never be allowed to become acid. It is best to keep it alkaline, hard, and somewhat salty. It should be clean and well aerated. Aeration is also of major importance to the incubating female. In dirty or stagnant water it is quite common for them to spit out the eggs. It also seems likely that the eggs that were spat out were dead, probably due to the high bacterial count in dirty water.

Some female mbuna have been known to spit out the eggs for brief periods of feeding, and then fail to pick them up again. The aquarist usually does not know whether the spat-out eggs are dead or merely abandoned. Thus, it is worthwhile to attempt to incubate these mouthbrooder eggs artificially. It has been done! Kappy Sprenger has had excellent results artificially incubating eggs of *Pseudotropheus auratus*. She uses a weak salt solution plus acriflavine and methylene blue. Dick Stratton also uses this method.

Pseudotropheus tropheops.

The *Haplochromis* species, like the mbunas and the American cichlids, habitually dig into and move the gravel in their aquaria. In the African pit spawners which become mouthbrooders during or immediately after spawning, movement of the gravel seems to be associated with setting up a spawning site. Gravel-moving tendencies are for the most part restricted to males among the *Haplochromis* species, and once a male begins his excavations he may continue the activity for days. The action might indicate that he is ready to spawn, but it is not necessarily indicative of the readiness of any nearby female to join him. Digging into the gravel is also associated with a search for small worms and other bits of food and is stimulated by feeding dry food in the aquarium.

These fishes seem to breed more frequently if there are a number of the same species in the same tank, rather than just a pair. A fresh water change often triggers excitement, leading to the female deciding to go ahead after all. Large tanks are preferred, as these are all very active fishes. Exceptions to keeping numerous males of one species include *P. auratus* and *P. elongatus*, both species being quite belligerent to their own kind. Males of most other species get along much better.

There is great infraspecific color variation. *Pseudotropheus zebra* exists as a regular (blue with black stripes), a cobalt blue, a white, and a mottled strain. All are found naturally in the lake. *L. trewavasae* may be blue, blue with a red or orange dorsal, or dirty gray. Females are often mottled orange, but may be gray. *L. fuelleborni* may be blue with a powder blue dorsal, or with an orange dorsal. Even body shape may vary somewhat, possibly as a consequence of incubation temperature or diet.

In addition to the usual meats, all the mbuna should be fed some plant material as this is their major food in nature (for most of them).

There are many other bizarre cichlids in the lake, and some of them will certainly be imported, by public aquariums if not home aquarists. Some of them snatch scales from other fishes whose schools they infiltrate. Others eat eyes. These, of course, are not ideal for the community tank! But remember the days when the only piranhas you saw were in public aquaria! Times change and aquarists get richer and sillier.

There are very many beautiful species in Lake Malawi that have not yet been imported in any quantity, if at all. And we haven't even seen the *Haplochromis* species, which greatly outnumber the mbuna. And so my friends, the best is yet to come.

The other regional lakes

The clouds of insects seen over Lake Malawi are also seen over Lake Victoria, but there all similarity ends. The deepest parts of the lakes contain the settling deposits found in other lakes that don't turn over, but in Lake Victoria, at least, this mud doesn't decompose when held in the air. This is due to the presence of a mysterious microorganism, in ways intermediate between blue-green algae and bacteria. Only when the mud is boiled to kill these strange organisms will the mud subsequently decompose. And so the mud of Lake Victoria keeps on accumulating, rather than participating, in

Julidochromis marlieri.

an easily measurable cycle. As a consequence of this (and the other lakes have similar nutrient problems), it is only the fringes of the lakes (the shoreline) and the surface waters that contain abundant fishes; *Tilapia* and their predators predominate in the open waters where the former may feed on plankton. The *Haplochromis* species, their derivatives, and a few other cichlids occupy the shore waters.

It was pointed out that most of the lake water comes from rain, although there is some stream contribution. Further, most of the loss of water from the lakes occurs through evaporation. One would expect the lakes to be, thereby, rather salty. But they are not nearly as saline as expected. Perhaps the nutrient settling takes up much of the mineral matter and keeps the salinity down.

The cichlids of Lake Edward and Lake Kivu were described in Ann. Mag. Nat. Hist., series 9, vol. 8, p. 632 in 1921. Those of Lake

Tropheus moorei.

Pseudotropheus zebra,

Julidochromis ornatus.

Haplochromis wingati.

Hemihaplochromis multicolor spawning in flowerpot.

Lamprologus leleupi.

Julidochromis ornatus.

Hemihaplochromis multicolor

Julidochromis marlieri.

Tropheus moorei.

Tanganyika were described in the same journal in 1920, on p. 30. Lake Albert contains only three species, *Tilapia nilotica, Haplochromis wingati,* and *H. multicolor* (or *Hemihaplochromis multicolor* if you prefer). As expected, *T. nilotica* is widely distributed in Africa and occurs in Lake Edward and Lake Kivu also. Lake Edward has another *Tilapia,* five *Haplochromis,* and other *Haplochromis*-like species. Lake Kivu has five endemic *Haplochromis* species. Lake Tanganyika, the largest of the Rift Valley lakes, has 34 genera with 134 species! We are already familiar with some of them, including *Tropheus moorei, Julidochromis marlieri, J. ornatus, Lamprologus compressiceps,* and *L. leleupi.* These Tanganyikan species are slowly becoming available to aquarists, but the demand far outstrips the supply at present.

One should not omit Lake Victoria species from consideration. Boulenger's catalogue of African Freshwater Fishes recognized 47,

Lamprologus leleupi.

Tropheus duboisi.

Lamprologus compressiceps.

Lamprologus mocquardi.

Lamprologus leleupi.

Labeotropheus trewavasae male.

and Regan in 1922 recognized 50 species. Regan furthermore considered all but one of the 50 to be endemic! Forty-four of these were
Haplochromis, and four of the five others were closely related to that
huge genus. Today we recognize 127 species in six genera. And so
it is abundantly clear that the genus *Haplochromis*, in all its African
diversity, is going to be the real source of excitement for years
to come.

Greenwood (1964) attempted to explain the enormous number of
Haplochromis species in Lakes Malawi, Tanganyika, and Victoria.
He also considered other lakes, including Lake Rudolf in Kenya.
His data are presented in Table 5.

The size of a lake is not necessarily a good indicator of the
number of species. Instead, one must look at the lake's variation,
and determine whether one lake has more diverse habitats which
could be occupied by different kinds of fishes. And it seems that
Lake Victoria does not have the diversity of available habitats that

TABLE 5
Data for some African lakes and their cichlids

	Tang.	Malawi	Vict.	Edward	Albert	Rudolf
All cichlid species	134	193	127	28	9	5
Endemic cichlid species	132	189	124	20	4	2
Cichlid genera	34	23	6	4	2	3
Endemic cichlid genera	30	20	4	1	0	0
Maximum lake depth (feet)	4,708	2,579	270	3,000	2,030	219
Area (square miles)	12,700	11,000	26,000	700	1,640	3,300

Lamprologus savoryi.

can be found in Lake Tanganyika, for example. Different types of beach (rock, shingle, sand, mud), different types of shoreline (steep, sloping, rocky, barren, overgrown with mangroves), all play a role in speciation.

To look at the fish, one generally could not determine why one species is found in one locale and another species elsewhere. They vary in coloration to be sure, as well as in teeth. Only the few deep water (exceptional) species are obviously adapted to their surroundings, with big eyes, etc.

Tilapia mariae guarding eggs (above) and fry; opposite, the fry in various stages of growth.

And so, why did these fishes undergo this explosive speciation in some of these lakes and not in others? And why did it happen at all? Let's first examine *Haplochromis* technically, and then in its diversity. The pharyngeal structure is formed in a specific way from two major bone types. The scales are ctenoid (remember that they were cycloid in *Tilapia*!). The teeth are in at least two rows in the front, tending to one row toward the sides. The shape of the teeth is very variable and useful on the species, not the genus, level.

Whereas many of the mbuna were plant feeders, in common with most *Tilapia* species, the genus *Haplochromis* contains plant feeders and predators also. In fact, about 40% of the *Haplochromis* feed on other fishes, frequently other *Haplochromis*! We have already indicated some of the bizarre types of feeding habits (eyeball eaters in L. Victoria; scale snatchers in L. Malawi). Would you believe kidnappers? There are *Haplochromis* species that engulf the snout of a brooding female and force her to expulse her eggs or fry into the mouth of the kidnapping species, which then eats them. This

Egyptian mouthbrooder female showing distended mouth and sunken belly after period of fasting while holding spawn.

is of some aquarium interest, knowing that they can be induced to release their brood. When removing a female that has just spat out her fry, it is a good idea to hold her underwater in the net, against the side of the aquarium, and shake her considerably to agitate her. If she still has any fry in her mouth, she will often let them go, and you will have saved some fry from possible loss in the recuperating tank (which may have other recuperating females, starting to eat everything in sight).

Greenwood and other authors have presented different ideas to explain the speciation. Most agree that the mouthbrooding habit has played a major role, by negating the importance of the pair bond (which can hold down a good male from serving the cause of population to the fullest). When one outstanding or better male can mate with many successive females, his progeny will quickly play a major role in the total population. Some hold that the diverse species originated as localized river populations which eventually were forced into the lake by periods of drought. Color and other species-specific signs were developed to retain the identity of the different forms forced into the same housing project. If the history of the lake is one of periodic fluctuations in the water level, allowing river mouth colonization repeatedly, and then destroying that habitat repeatedly, the number of different populations would rapidly increase. The history of these big lakes does indicate that rises and falls have occurred rather frequently. In fact, the mouthbrooding habit itself is seen as a biological answer to water level fluctuations. In times of drought, the nests at the shoreline would be desiccated. But if the fish are mouthbrooders, they can carry their progeny to safety.

If we start with a fish that has characteristics of both nesters and mouthbrooders (such as some *Tilapia* we spoke about earlier, or *Geophagus jurupari*), then it is clear how the mouthbrooding habit came to have a selective advantage over other methods of brooding. And so it seems to be a combination of unstable water levels and the potential for mouthbrooding which have resulted in the great diversity of species and their predominantly mouthbrooding habit. The paper by Greenwood is required reading for cichlidophiles.

Something must be said about *egg spots* in mouthbrooders. Wickler (1966c) has suggested, and it has been popularized as if it were proven fact, that the egg spots or little yellow marks on the

→ *Haplochromis desfontainesi*

Haplochromis burtoni.

The "egg spots" on the anal fin of these *Haplochromis* don't really look much like the species' eggs and are distributed away from, rather than toward, the vent.

anal fin of the male mouthbrooder have a particular function. This function is to fool the female into snapping at them, thereby inhaling sperm and assuring fertilization. Wickler said that the spots resemble the eggs of the species in color, size and form. I would suggest that *this is not true in all cases.*

Eggs of several mbuna are ovoid, yellowish white, and of constant sizes and shapes. On the other hand, egg spots tend to be rather bright yellow, of varying sizes and shapes, and restricted to the outermost part of the fin in both males and females. The female *P. zebra*, which I have observed closely on numerous spawning occasions, does not snap at the region of the spots (the end of the anal), but picks up eggs which tend to be concentrated right at the male's vent, which is at the front of the anal fin. Wickler may yet be on the right track, but I personally doubt it.

The proper experiment would be to obliterate the part of the anal fin containing the spots, to determine if this interferes with fish productivity. Hypotheses are much better when they are based on experimentation.

9. AMERICAN CICHLIDS

Cichlids in the New World are found from Texas, along the eastern and southern coasts of Mexico, to Central and most of South America and some of the Caribbean islands. The lone native U.S. species is *Cichlasoma cyanoguttata*, a large and beautiful fish found in the same waters with centrarchids (the basses and sunfishes). Exotics have been introduced into various American waters.

A few genera are very familiar to aquarists, e.g., *Aequidens, Cichla, Cichlasoma, Herotilapia, Apistogramma, Nannacara, Geophagus, Astronotus, Crenicichla, Pterophyllum,* and *Symphysodon.* These genera will be discussed individually. One generalization can be made: these fishes are all substrate spawners. Some dig pits in sand or gravel, others clean a hard surface for spawning, and others may subsequently pick up the eggs for mouthbrooding after a long time exposure to the open terrain habitat. Except for these belated mouthbrooders (*Geophagus jurupari* and perhaps some others in the genus), and the fishes we know little or nothing about, all the American cichlids then fall into two categories of interest to the breeder: pit spawners, and hard substrate spawners. The hard substrate may be a flowerpot, rock, strip of slate, or the leaf of a large plant, e.g., *Echinodorus* spp. For such fishes artificial incubation is usually possible and more successful than natural incubation by the parents. An exception is *Symphysodon,* in which the fry are heavily dependent on parental slime secretions. See also the section on Asian cichlids.

Cichlasoma cyanoguttata guarding young. The young Texas cichlids gather around their parent.

Cichlasoma cyanoguttata, showing the frontal gibbosity that enlarges as the fish ages.

Cichlasoma erythraeum.

Cichlasoma cyanoguttata guarding eggs.

Giant American cichlids

Some of the American forms of the family Cichlidae normally achieve too great a size for the average home aquarium. Many of the *Crenicichla*, in addition, are quite rough and not desirable. Our own Texas cichlid, *Cichlasoma cyanoguttata*, while developing a beautiful stardust blue and white pattern, achieves rather a large size (about the same as our native crappie). Although a peaceful fish, its room requirements demand that it tie up too much tank space, and so many Texas aquarists keep young ones, but do not attempt to keep large adults. This species may also be a pit spawner, making artificial handling of eggs unfeasible. Axelrod claims they are substrate spawners in the aquarium. In nature, I have observed them spawning in large nesting communities in deep water, while the native centrarchids (sunfishes, etc.) tended to occupy the shoreline sand areas.

Cichla ocellaris is a very large fish, much prized as a gamefish in South America where it is the equivalent of our own largemouth and smallmouth basses. In general shape, finnage and coloration, it

Immature *Astronotus ocellatus.*

These almost-adult *A. ocellatus* have assumed their mature coloration, considerably different from the marbled pattern of the young oscars shown opposite.

Cichla ocellaris, young specimen.

Cichlasoma hellabrunni, often called *C. coryphaenoides*.

Astronotus ocellatus herding their young.

The red devils are among the most avid diggers of the family and are very efficient at their gravel-moving tasks.

Cichlasoma dovii.

reminds one of our native yellow perch. *Cichlasoma managuense* is attractive, but not beautiful and therefore not worth the space. And the same may be said for some other species. Some large cichlids are indeed attractive, such as *Cichlasoma dovii* (in several color phases) and the red devils (*C. labiatum, C. erythraeum,* and others), but these rather rough fishes are again kept mainly by connoisseurs. The chocolate cichlid, *C. hellabrunni* (often called *C. coryphaenoides,* a smaller fish) is very peaceful and popular. Not quite as docile, but even more popular is the oscar or velvet cichlid, *Astronotus ocellatus.* This giant is a hard substrate spawner and often kept and bred by aquarists. It has been (accidentally) introduced into Florida waters, where it is appreciated by fishermen as the peacock eye bass. The state game and fish people are not quite so appreciative! Several other cichlids achieve rather a large size, and in many cases the coloration warrants their keeping only at such sizes; hence, they too are only for the fanatically dedicated aquarist with large aquaria available.

Cichlasoma managuense.

Cichlasoma hellabrunni, the "real" chocolate cichlid. Visible at top left in this photo is *Herotilapia multispinosa*.

A new strain of *Astronotus ocellatus*; popularly known as red oscars, these fish are being developed at Gulf Fish Farms.

It must be emphasized that what fishes do in nature often has no relevance to what they do in aquaria. Thus, a number of pit spawners (in nature) will spawn on the bare slate of the aquarium or may choose to spawn on a hard surface in the aquarium. As far as I can determine, no matter where they spawn, the eggs are nonetheless slightly or very adhesive. Under such circumstances, it is *possible* (but inconvenient) to artificially handle the eggs. Some fish, however, are adamant in their demands for a pit and are generally difficult to induce to spawn.

Dwarf American cichlids

Two genera supply most of our dwarfs: *Nannacara* with two species, and *Apistogramma* with many species (usually difficult to identify). A number of dwarfs are also found in the genus *Aequidens*, but this is generally not considered a dwarf genus. Because the behavior of the dwarfs generally parallels that of the larger cichlids, they are ideal laboratory animals, requiring little space. Another advantage is that a camera may be set up to cover a limited space where everything occurs, and this would be next to impossible with their larger brethren. Much of our quantitative knowledge of cichlid behavior is based on studies with *Nannacara anomala* and several species of *Apistogramma*. Ethologists continue to use larger cichlids still, probably because they are hardier, longer lived, and exhibit generally more complex behavior.

The genus *Nannacara*

Two species are known to the hobby, *Nannacara anomala* and *N. taenia*. The latter species is rare in the hobby and is reported from the Amazon. Perhaps its rarity is just another case of our not recognizing it when we see it, hence the lack of breeding reports in the popular literature. On the other hand, *N. anomala* is easily recognized; this species was reported from western Guyana and Venezuela. The two species cannot be separated simply on counts.

N. anomala	*N. taenia*
D. XVI–XVII/7–8	D. XVI/7
A. III–IV/7–8	A. III/7
L1. 23–24	L1. 24

A breeding account of *N. anomala* was given by Goldstein (1967). Popularly called the golden-eye dwarf cichlid, a better name might be the slate or gray dwarf cichlid to indicate the usual color of the male. Males attain larger size than females, usually over two inches, although larger than three inches is not unusual. Females are considerably smaller, average adult size being under $1\frac{1}{2}$ inches. They may be kept in their own five gallon tank or in a community tank, and will spawn with equal likelihood in both places. Prior to spawning the male develops his best nuptial colors and is rather rough on the female. After spawning, which occurs in a rock cave, flowerpot, or on a rock out in the open (if nothing else is available), the tables are turned. The female becomes the dangerous partner and the male is driven off. In a small aquarium he may be badly beaten by his diminutive mate, and should be removed.

The sexual dimorphism and dichromatism between male and female *Nannacara anomala* is especially pronounced. The larger, showier fish at right is the male.

The female takes care of the eggs and fry and may be considered an excellent parent. If spawning occurs in a community tank, the male is safe, but the fry will gradually be snapped up one by one by the other tankmates despite the best efforts of the female. Thus, it is best to remove the eggs for artificial hatching. In tanks where it is difficult to tell whether spawning has occurred, the best clue to its having happened is the pattern of the female. After spawning has taken place, she develops a marked checkerboard pattern and spends most of her time with the eggs, coming out occasionally to see that the vicinity is clear of hostiles. The eggs hatch in 2 to 3 days, and the fry are free-swimming in an additional five days. They should be started on newly hatched brine shrimp and microworms. The fry behave as a shoal, and if the female is left with them she will herd them carefully to and from feeding and resting areas. Juvenile females of this species will also herd and protect groups of fry of unrelated cichlids, including *Apistogramma* and *Pelmatochromis*.

Nannacara anomala, male above.

Nannacara anomala eggs.

Nannacara taenia.

The genus *Apistogramma*

This large genus of usually difficult-to-identify species ranges through most of South America. Some are pit spawners (e.g., *A. ramirezi*), but most are hard surface spawners. Their identification is a headache even for ichthyologists. Only a few species are easily recognized. See Table 6 for some data. Not included is *A. hoignei* Meinken, 1965.

TABLE 6
Species of *Apistogramma* Regan and some data

	Dorsal	Anal	Pelvics	Lateral line
A. agassizi	XV/7	III/4	14	23
A. ambloplitoides	XIII/10	III/9	13	—
A. amoenum	—	—	—	—
A. borelli	XVI/5–6	III/6–7	—	18–22
A. cacatuoides	—	—	—	—
A. corumbae	XVI/6	III/6–7	11	22
A. klausewitzi	—	—	—	—
A. kleei	—	—	—	—
A. ornatipinnis	XV/7–8	III/6	—	21–24
A. ortmanni	XV/7	III/6–7	12	22–24
A. pertense	XVI/6	III/6	12–13	23
A. pleurotaenia	XVI/6	IV/5	—	23
A. ramirezi	XIV–XV/9	III/8	11–12	26–29
A. reitzigi	XVI/5	III/5	—	21
A. steindachneri	—	—	—	—
A. trifasciatum	—	—	—	—
A. weisei	XVI/6	III/4	—	22
A. wickleri	—	—	—	—

It is hopeless for an aquarist to attempt to identify members of this genus merely on counts. Measurement data, in the hands of the aquarist, may not shed any light on an already confused situation. It is best to pickle the fish and send them off to the United States National Museum (Smithsonian Institution) after death. But during life, all the aquarist can do is compare his fish with published photographs. It is important to have a set of photos of all species in the genus known to the hobby. Identifications must be based on excellent agreement between fish and photo. The photo which 'best fits

Apistogramma ortmanni.

Apistogramma reitzigi.

Apistogramma trifasciatum, male (above) and xanthistic form of female.

Apistogramma borelli, male above.

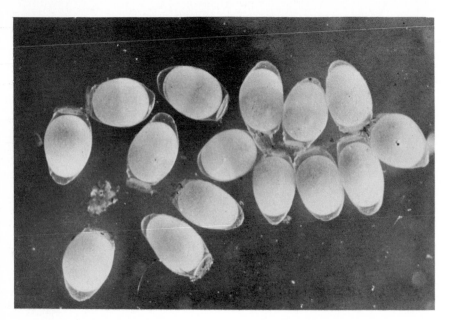

Eggs of *Apistogramma ortmanni*.

the fish' is likely wrong. Many aquarists think they can identify a fish by the color of its eggs. That is incorrect. The color of the eggs is determined by lipids (fats and oils) in the diet, and is not a useful criterion for identification. If you switch diets on your fish, you can manipulate the colors of their eggs, albeit in unpredictable ways.

Most *Apistogramma* species require warmth, clean water, and privacy. It is best to set up pairs in 7 gallon aquaria. The tanks should be in a heated room or contain heaters; there should be sand or gravel (preferably sand) in the tank, some rooted plants, and a flowerpot or facsimile. Subsand filtration is desirable. A few small tetras or livebearers (e.g., *Heterandria formosa*) will help them adapt to the new surroundings. Good lighting is beneficial, but it should not be overdone. Floating water sprite will cut down on glare and also serve as an indicator of water quality. The bulk of the diet should be living. Tubifex worms are ideal, but brine shrimp are also excellent. Occasional feedings of mosquito larvae or chironomids will be worth the effort to collect them. If these live foods are not

142

Apistogramma haraldschultzi.

Spawning pair of *Apistogramma ramirezi*; the female is of the color variety popularly called golden ram.

Apistogramma pertense.

Apistogramma ortmanni.

available, then shrimp eggs should be hatched, and nauplii fed the adult fishes. Prepared foods should be fed with care, as *Apistogramma* species are not heavy eaters. But they are susceptible to disease in fouled aquaria; hence the accent on living foods.

These fishes may be kept in large aquaria as colonies. Some species (e.g., *A. ramirezi*) usually spawn in a pit, and many pairs may set up housekeeping in the same large tank. Most species, however, prefer a form of cave (flowerpot, coconut shell) and privacy, and the small tank is preferred for them. The site is prepared by both parents, although the female will often undertake care of the spawn all by herself. *Apistogramma* species are not as belligerently protective of the young as *Nannacara*, and may abandon them under stress. (Neither are they pugnacious toward their own or other species, and may be considered good community tank fishes with other *unrelated* species of the same approximate size.) Since the females and sometimes the males of these dwarfs may be confused, it is a good idea not to mix your stock in the same aquaria unless there are clear differences between the different forms. The fry should be given microworms at first, followed by brine shrimp nauplii. They grow slowly, although they haven't far to go!

As these fishes are not the best of parents, it is advisable to handle the first couple of spawnings artificially to assure that you have some offspring. Spawnings run to around 150 eggs, but one raises about 30 to 50 fish after all the mortality, most of which occurs among the eggs. Some species are ready and prolific spawners *(pertense, pleurotaenia, ramirezi)*, whereas others are not as quick to spawn *(agassizi)*, although they will—seemingly grudgingly! All are susceptible to bacterial infections in dirty water. Thus, keep the sand surface clean, the water clear, warm, and well-aerated, and the plants lighted and happy. If the tank looks like part of a forest brook, the fish should look good too. These fishes will not tolerate laxity in aquarium management.

There is a golden strain of *A. ramirezi* available. This is merely a strain fixed from a mutant or sport; it is entitled to no special name other than golden *Apistogramma ramirezi*.

A few species of this genus are pronounced atrociously by most aquarists. Here is some recommended phonetic spelling.

ramirezi	RAM-EAR'-EZ-EYE
agassizi	AG'-UH-SEE-EYE
reitzigi	RIGHT'-ZIG-EYE
kleei	CLAY'-EYE
wickleri	VIK'-LRR-EYE

As yet unidentified *Apistogramma* species.

Summary of American dwarfs

All species require only small aquaria, but some may be kept in communities in larger tanks. Generally the female is the parent who exercises responsibility for the offspring. These fishes are not very aggressive, except for *Nannacara anomala*, in which the female is belligerent when brooding. Best results obtain with artificial handling of the eggs, but *Nannacara* may be trusted as a good parent. The color of the eggs means nothing in identification, nor does the usual employment of simple counts. Photos are the most reliable method, if the photos are good. Pictures with a yellow or blue cast should be discarded as unreliable. All species require cleanliness, and live food is recommended for the bulk of the diet. The dwarfs are not diggers, and rooted plants may be kept in their tanks. Sand is preferred to gravel for (1) cleanliness and (2) keeping the babies and their food above the substrate where they belong. Warmth and good light are recommended, as is undergravel (subsand) filtration.

147

Apistogramma corumbae.

Apistogramma reitzigi.

Apistogramma cacatuoides.

Apistogramma agassizi.

Geophagus australe.

Geophagus surinamensis.

Geophagus brasiliensis.

The genus *Geophagus*

This has been a confused genus for many years, at one time containing species now in *Apistogramma* or elsewhere. The distribution
ranges from Panama in Central America to Argentina in southern
South America. The genus is characterized by the form of the gill
arches, by the great distance of the lateral line from the dorsal fin,
and by the end of the lateral line, where it enters the caudal, being
divided (bifurcate). These fishes are all diggers, and have well-
shaped snouts for that particular purpose. They are medium to
large cichlids and should have large aquaria with much coarse
gravel. Outside filtration is preferred.

The most popular species is *G. jurupari*, but much of what has
been written about it may refer to the very similar *G. acuticeps*,
which has long, pointy ventrals. The next most popular species is

Apistogramma klausewitzi.

Apistogramma ambloplitoides.

Apistogramma steindachneri.

G. brasiliensis. Other species include *G. australe*, *G. gymnogenys*, and *G. surinamensis*. Closely related to *Geophagus* is *Biotodoma*, with one species, *B. cupido*. See Table 7 for counts. Other species in *Geophagus* include *G. wavrini*, *G. daemon*, and *G. campoensis*.

TABLE 7
Comparison of *Geophagus* and *Biotodoma* species

	Dorsal	Anal	Lateral line
B. cupido	XV/10	III/9	29–31
G. acuticeps	XIII–XIV/11–12	III/7–8	30–31
G. australe	XII–XIV/10–11	III/8	25–27
G. brasiliensis	XIV–XVI/10–13	III/8–9	27–30
G. gymnogenys	XIII–XIV/10–11	III/9	27–30
G. jurupari	XV–XVI/9–10	III/6–7	29–31
G. surinamensis	XVII–XIX/11–13	III/7	33–36

Most aquarists can recognize *G. brasiliensis* and *G. jurupari*. And now they can also recognize *G. acuticeps*, if not from what has just been said of the ventrals, then from the same information in Innes. *G. surinamensis* is easily recognized by the shape of its head; convex, but taking a concave dip over the eyes, which thereby seem to protrude. I have seen what appears to be nondescript species of *Geophagus*, and these may have been *G. australe*, if this summary of the genus is complete. *Biotodoma* has a large spot on the upper flanks at about the junction of the spiny and soft dorsals. The spot is dark, ringed with white, or slightly bordered with white. It also has numerous vertical double-bands along the sides. A comprehensive report on this species was given by Loiselle (1967).

Except for *G. jurupari* and *B. cupido*, all the others are regular substrate breeders. *B. cupido* is said to be a mouthbrooder, but no breeding reports are known in the hobby literature in this country. *G. jurupari* begins as a substrate breeder in the usual sense, but about 24 hours after spawning both parents pick up the eggs for oral incubation. This incubation period lasts about eight days. However, the parents may accept the young into their mouths (e.g., during periods of danger) for up to 30 days. See Myrberg (1965).

Most members of this group (with the exception of *G. brasiliensis*) are not ready spawners, and for this reason artificial incubation is recommended for all but the two mouthbrooders.

Pterophyllum scalare.

The genera *Pterophyllum* and *Symphysodon*

In the early stages of the aquarium hobby, the angel fish was truly the king of the aquarium. Eventually, it gave way to the discus fish. Throughout their histories in the hobby, both fishes have undergone considerable nit-picking about their valid names. I would like to present my opinion at this time, after giving some of the history of the name changes.

For many years the common angel was called *Pterophyllum scalare*, or the 'angel' or 'scalare.' The great aquarist C. H. Peters, writing in *The Home Aquarium Bulletin* for 1934, used the term 'Scalare,' and his article is still one of the most complete, albeit brief, discussions of this fish. Later, Innes, in his *Exotic Aquarium Fishes*, used the name *P. eimekei*, distinguishing it from *P. scalare* and stating that this latter species was seldom seen in the hobby. Recently, Schultz (1967) considered that both nominal species were

Geophagus brasiliensis.

Geophagus acuticeps.

Biotodoma (formerly *Geophagus*) *cupido.*

Acarichthys heckelii (synonym *A. thayeri*).

one and the same. Since *P. scalare* was the older name, it took priority, and is now the valid name of the angel fish. There are two other species in the genus, *P. dumerilii* and *P. altum*. The latter is sometimes seen in the hobby (although still not commercially bred), and may be recognized by its uneven snout profile. Therefore, our discussion of angel fish must be restricted to *P. scalare*.

We tended to think of angels as hard to breed until recently, when it seemed that every novice was having success. In fact, even Peters said in 1934, "The falling price is due to the fact that thousands of them are propagated each year in the United States and added thousands are sent to us from foreign breeders. Scalare are no longer considered difficult to breed." Peters also discussed sexing angels by (1) the breeding tube (as most people do today) and (2) the shape of the vent (large and oval in the female and small and circular in the male). Anyone who has bred angels knows that the spawning tube of the female is massive and blunt, while that of the male is fine and pointed. Many authors have tried to sex angels by the shape of the lower profile, and by the angularity of the ventral (pelvic) fins. I consider these latter approaches a waste of time. Most angel breeders can sex their own stock, but are at a loss to sex anyone else's stock. It's really a matter of eyeballing your own fish and guessing, on behavior as much as on anything else, which are the males and females. Few breeders can tell you *how they know*, but their "guesstimates" are usually quite sharp.

There has also been a profusion of strains of angels within the last ten years, and this certainly reflects the enormity of successful breeding operations going on around the world. Who can guess the number of angels sold annually? The old angel is now the *silver angel*. From this fish there was developed, independently, a dark variety and a longer finned variety. Quickly these two strains were brought together. The darker fish containing elongated finnage was called the *lace angel*. Darkness was fixed into blackness, and we subsequently got the *black angel*. In no time, the two strains were combined into the *black lace angel*. Working in the other direction (loss of color), a strain appeared around 1965–66 that was dubbed the *blushing angel*. This strain lacks dark markings on the body and silver coloring on the operculum; hence the gills show through. I personally would have dubbed this fish the *culled angel* (and discarded such stock), but some clever breeder tacked on the name

Pterophyllum scalare.

159

Geophagus jurupari.

This *Geophagus* shows affinities to both *G. surinamensis* and *G. australe*, but the horizontal lines in the caudal fin make it unlike any *Geophagus* known to hobbyists.

Geophagus surinamensis, juvenile.

The most recent marbleized angelfish, developed by William Ash.

blushing, and proceeded to popularize the strain. A fairly recent introduction is the *marble angel,* and one wonders why it took so long to arrive on the scene. Most recent of all is the golden angel.

In the future we may expect breeders to take advantage of the high content of green in some strains of black lace angels and lace angels, and come up with a green angel. That will truly be a fish worth having. In general, the black fish are not as hardy as the wild type or silver angel. The reasons are not known, but I would suggest a relationship to the fish's needs for the amino acid *phenylalanine.* This amino acid (one of the building blocks of protein) is needed for melanin formation (the black pigment is melanin). Perhaps so much phenylalanine is diverted to melanin production that there is not enough for other important functions, unless the diet is very rich in this specific compound. Indeed, most of the loss of black angels occurs at about the same age (dime to nickel sized

Juvenile angelfishes.

body) in any one spawning, and this points to a dietary or other metabolic disorder. I would suggest raising angels of the black varieties on very high protein diets. Black strains of mollies historically have been much more fragile than the wild types, and this may be further evidence for this point of view, i.e., the requirement for phenylalanine. The hypothesis can easily be tested, and is herein offered as just that, not as a theory.

Angels also have been developed with longer than normal fins. These are called veil angels. All color varieties, except *blushing* and golden, have been bred with veils.

The oldest known published color photograph of parent angels and their growing young.

A wild-caught *P. scalare*.

Pterophyllum dumerilii.

The names of discus fish have been tossed hither and yon in recent years, and I'd like to throw it back! It is generally accepted that there are two species of discus fish, *Symphysodon discus* and *S. aequifasciata*. The latter occurs in many color phases, and Schultz has applied subspecific names to these color forms.

Both angels and discus can be bred in any reasonable kind of water conditions. The general tendency, however, is to keep angels in somewhat alkaline water and discus in slightly acid water. If the water is very acidic, neither fish are happy, although acid water tends to keep the protozoan (and possibly bacterial) concentration down. Angels are kept in moderately hard to hard water, and discus in soft water. Again, these conditions seem more a matter of personal taste and reliance on the literature than on trial and error. In any case, raising the fishes from young in your own tanks will assure that the adults are adapted to your particular set-ups. Frequent partial water changes are advisable with both species, and the water should not be dechlorinated if *chlorine* is used by your city water department. If *chloramine* is used, you may prefer to dechlorinate with commercial sodium thiosulfate ('chlorine remover'). A mild exposure to chlorine seems to act as a tonic to the fish, perhaps by attacking the bacteria in the tank, and perhaps in other ways. In either case, it won't hurt anything. *Phone your water department.*

Both species should be raised in large aquaria with gentle current, and not with very heavy aeration. These fishes come from quiet waters and are not built to fight a current. One side of the tank should have large, heavy-leaved plants, and there should be an open clearing as well. The fish are substrate spawners, but their substrate is well removed from the bottom of the tank. Plants are preferred, but the breeder may prefer to operate in smaller aquaria with a strip of slate as the egg surface. The slate is placed on end, standing in the tank. Both parents clean the surface and protect the territory as spawning time approaches. You can keep your fish in a large show tank until they stake out their territory, and then move them, if preferred, to a spawning tank.

For angels, this need not be larger than 10 gallons (depending on the size of the fish). Discus should have at least twice as much room, as they are shy in cramped quarters. After considerable scrubbing of the spawning site, for many days usually, the actual event occurs. The spawning tubes are visible a few days prior to actual spawning,

A mature pair of *S. aequifasciata*, brown form, in excellent condition.

and it is not a good idea to move fish whose tubes are down (exposed). The male's tube is fine and small, and the female's is broad and blunt. The fish take turns passing over the spawning site, depositing their gametes (eggs and sperm).

The novice may now prefer to let the parents raise the young. In discus breeding, this is almost a requirement. The fry need to feed on the slime secreted by the surface of both parents, and few breeders have succeeded in raising young discus artificially. A notable exception is Jack Wattley of Florida, who has developed a method not yet published. Until that time, most of us have to rely on the parents to care for the young and feed them, and this is a risky business. It usually takes a number of spawnings before the parent fish learn not to eat the young! Brooding discus should not be disturbed, and this means *no visitors* to the fish room. Try showing off your eggs and you often as not will end up with a lost spawn.

Angels are less temperamental. But they can be raised artificially and this is the method of choice for two reasons. First, you guarantee

An albino angelfish.

The blushing angel.

Parent *Symphysodon aequifasciata*, brown form, tend their newly hatched young, which are clinging to leaf of large Amazon sword plant.

The fry have become free-swimming and graze off their parents' bodies.

Black lace veil angel.

Pterophyllum altum.

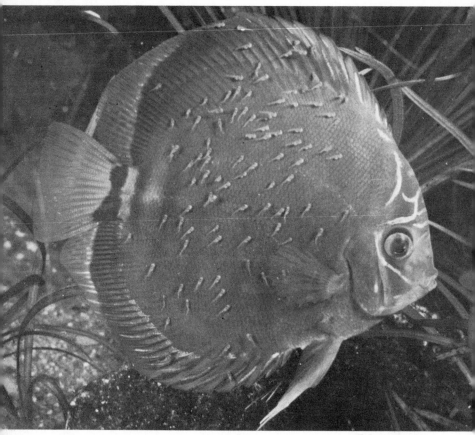

Young *S. aequifasciata*, brown form, taking nourishment from mucus on side of parent fish.

that the eggs will not be eaten, and secondly, the fish will spawn again much sooner if they are not taking care of a family. To *see* an angel family, however, is a sight not to be forgotten, and you can trust to the parents if this is your goal.

The slate or the leaf containing the eggs should be removed about a half day or more after spawning is completed, and placed in a gallon jar or two-gallon drum bowl with tank water. Add enough methylene blue to totally darken the water until you can hardly see your hand on the other side. Place the jar in a large paper bag on a shelf or table and set an airstone next to and slightly below the eggs. Turn up the air to a moderate stream. If too fast, it will knock the

Here the young discus are about to transfer from one parent to the other; male and female discus take turns in presenting their bodies to be eaten from.

fry off upon hatching, and if too weak it will not dispel the gases of metabolism. The eggs hatch in about three days, and the fry are free-swimming in four to six more days depending on temperature. Microworms or newly hatched live brine shrimp are the first food, and brine shrimp can be the main or total dietary component until the fish are dime size. Then you can go to cheaper fare. For black angels, use a lot of meats as soon as they can take them. Young discus should be removed from the parents as soon as they are taking brine shrimp in quantity. Fry of both species should be raised in aquaria without gravel. Sand or bare bottoms are preferred.

Deformities are common among angel fish, and these are prob-

Naja's golden angel.

The marble angel.

Male parent discus with young feeding from both sides of body.

Considerably older here, the fry continue to nibble from parents' bodies, but at this size they have become much more adventurous and harder for the parents to keep in line.

Symphysodon aequifasciata, brown form; these are tank-bred fish.

Young tank-bred *S. aequifasciata*, brown form.

A trio of well-maintained discus.

The discus at left is in the process of shaking off the young so that they will take up the feeding position on the other parent.

S. aequifasciata, brown form, at about two months of age.

In South America, discus often are taken as food fish; here noted ethnologist/explorer Harald Schultz eats discus that died during transport after being collected.

A discus photographed very shortly after having been taken from its home waters.

Symphysodon discus at right, *S. aequifasciata*, green form, at left.

Symphysodon discus.

ably due to handling rather than to any inherited factors. Such fish
will probably be adequate breeders. The most common deformities
on angels are missing gill covers and notches in the profile. Commercial breeders discard such fish, as they don't sell. But who
knows? Perhaps soon we will see a new strain on the market called
the *notched angel*? Give it a name, and people will buy it!

   An all too common affliction of discus fish is the so-called discus
disease or *hole-in-the-head disease*. The cause of this disease remains

unknown to this day. It has variously been reported as due to protozoa, fungi, worms, and bacteria. I have examined a number of such diseased fishes, and have come up with some observations, but no firm conclusions. First, I have never found *Ichthyophonus* or known pathogenic bacteria in the carcasses. There are no worms. What looks like a worm is actually pus forming a string and flowing in the current around the fish's head. I have found what appears to be some kind of fungus in the livers of some of the fish, but it is unclear how this could possibly be related to the disease of the head, and I tend to consider it unrelated to discus disease, unless it is a predisposing factor (perhaps weakening them to invasion by something else). The holes in the head follow the general course of the frontal lateral line system, and may indeed be the result of infection of the nervous system. If this is the case, then the cause should be either bacterial or viral. I have not found the pus to contain bacteria; rather, it seems to flow at a remarkable rate and antibacterial dyes painted on the lesions are to no avail. The dyes are pushed out in a couple of hours by the fast-flowing pus. Pus streaked out on agar plates was sterile. A few aquarists have had success stopping the course of the disease with tetracyclines; these are wide-spectrum antibiotics. The best guess at this time is that we are dealing with bacteria infecting the nervous system around the head, but their numbers are very small in proportion to the damage they cause. Until the organism is isolated, however, we will not be able to do laboratory determinations of which antibiotics are most effective. It is also possible that a virus begins the damage, and the bacteria are secondary invaders. If this is the case, then we are in trouble, as there are practically no cures for viruses, and there are certainly none for fish viruses at present. Living infected discus fish should be sent to the Eastern Fish Diseases Laboratory, Kearneysville, West Virginia. Perhaps this able staff can come up with something positive. Because of the expense of working with discus fish, however, the cooperation of the hobbyist is required to defray costs.

Miscellaneous American genera

A number of genera are relatively unknown to aquarists, but their popularity should be anticipated as the demand for new and pretty fish continues to grow.

Crenicichla lepidota.

Crenicichla saxatilis surinamensis.

Discus strain developed by breeder Jack Wattley at Roberts Fish Farm; this strain is sold under the name Wattley's turquoise discus.

The eye bar of this discus has remained prominently dark even though the other bands show much less intensely than they normally do.

The brilliant blue vermiculations on the head of this brown discus make
it especially attractive; this is an old specimen.

Uaru amphiacanthoides.

Chaetobranchus Heckel contains two crappie-shaped yellowish species, *C. flavescens* and *C. bitaeniatus*. Neither has yet been reported as bred. *C. bitaeniatus* is said to be peaceful and not a digger.

The genus *Acaronia* (synonym: *Acaropsis*) contains two species, *A. nassa* and *A. trimaculata*. This genus is very close to *Aequidens*. They have not yet been reported as bred.

Uaru Heckel contains two species, *U. amphiacanthoides* and *U. imperialis*. They are said to spawn like Angels, but the young are difficult to raise. Perhaps parental slime is required.

Herotilapia contains one species, *H. multispinosa*. This is the new rainbow cichlid. It differs from *Cichlasoma* in having tricuspid teeth (whereas *Cichlasoma* has conical teeth). A very easy fish to breed and raise, it may rival the Congo or convict cichlid in popularity among

Herotilapia multispinosa.

beginning cichlidophiles. Although attaining about four inches, they will breed at 1½ inches.

Acarichthys Eigenmann contains one species, *A. heckelii.** This genus may prove to be a junior synonym for *Aequidens*.

Neetroplus nematopus was reported (Bussing, 1966) from the Atlantic drainage of Costa Rica.

Biotoecus from Brazil contains *B. opercularis*, and is seldom seen.

There are two pike-like genera, *Batrachops* and *Crenicichla*. In the former genus, the inner teeth are not depressible. *Batrachops* contains *B. cyanonotus*, *B. nemopterus*, and *B. reticulatus*.

Crenicichla contains a number of species (see Table 8). These appear to be pit spawners, with the male taking care of the spawn. Generally rough fishes, preferring lots of room and lots of plants for hiding.

---

* *A. heckelii*; a junior synonym is *A. thayeri*.

Chaetobranchus (often called *Chaetobranchopsis*) *bitaeniatus.*

Chaetobranchus flavescens.

Uaru amphiacanthoides.

Acaronia (synonym *Acaropsis*) *nassa.*

Crenichla lepidota specimen that has been maintained in an aquarium under good conditions for some time; freshly imported *Crenicichla* almost always arrive emaciated and badly battered.

TABLE 8
Some data for the genus *Crenicichla* Heckel.
(After Schultz, 1949)

	Dorsal	*Anal*	*Scale Rows*
C. anthurus	XXII/10	III/8	—
C. dorsocellata	XX–XXIII/10–13	III/8	62–65
C. lepidota	XVII–XVIII/13–14	III/8–10	45–60
C. saxatilis	XVII–XX/13–16	III/8–10	50–62
C. johanna	XXI–XXIV/16–17	III/11–12	97–107
C. alta	XVIII–XIX/13–15	III/9–10	58–69
C. geayi	XXII/11	III/8	57
C. wallacii	XX–XXI/9–11	III/7–9	57
C. macrophthalma	XX–XXII/10–13	III/7–9	62–70
C. lugubris	—	—	106–113
C. lucius	—	—	—
C. vittata	—	—	—
C. multispinosa	—	—	90–108
C. nana	—	—	38–72
C. lenticulata	—	—	112–130
C. ornata	17–19	—	112–130
C. strigata	15–17	—	112–130
C. notophthalma	—	—	—

Crenicara maculata bridges the gap between the dwarfs and the regular sized cichlids. Peaceful, very distinctive, and not rare. These cave-spawners sometimes are found in shipments of mixed dwarf cichlids; rarely are they correctly called checkerboard cichlids. Another species, *C. punctulata*, is known.

The genus *Petenia* Günther was named for the state of Peten in northern Guatemala, at the base of the Yucatan Peninsula. It contains three species, *P. krausii, P. spectabilis* and *P. myersi*. No aquarium data available. They are widely distributed from Central America into northern South America (Venezuela and Colombia).

The genus *Cichlasoma*

This is one of the largest genera of American cichlids, and contains a number of old aquarium favorites. Some authors still (Ouchynnyk, 1968) use the generic name *Cichlaurus* for a number of the species *(severum, ornatum, festae, autochthon)*, mainly because the author of both generic names, Swainson, used *Cichlaurus* earlier in the same paper in which he also used *Cichlasoma*. Most persons, however, prefer not to use *Cichlaurus* at all, including all the species in *Cichlasoma* Swainson.

Cichlasoma severum.

Crenicichla dorsocellata.

Crenicichla geayi.

Crenicichla geayi.

Crenicichla lenticulata.

Crenicichla lepidota.

Cichlasoma spilurum male.

Cichlasoma hellabrunni.

Young wild-caught *Cichlasoma severum*,

Cichlasoma centrarchus.

Crenicara maculata.

Biotecus opercularis.

Crenicichla wallacei.

Crenicara filamentosa.

South American fishermen on the hunt for cichlids native to their waters.

A partial listing of species would include the following: *alfari, altifrons, atromaculatum, adspersum, autochthon, arnoldi, aureum, beani, centrarchus, coryphaenoides, crassa, cyanoguttata, dovii, friedrichsthalii, festivum, facetum, fenestratum, haitiensis, hellabrunni, labiatum (citrinellum* may be a variety of this*), longimanus, maculicauda, meeki, motaguense, nigrofasciatum, octofasciatum* (syn., *biocellatus), ornatum, psitticum, ramsdeni, rostratum, salvini, sieboldi, spilotum, spilurum* (syn., *cutteri), severum, spectabile, terrabae, tuba, tetracanthus,* and *urophthalmus.*

Most of these species are Central American, some are Caribbean, and the remainder (except for the one U.S. species) are from farther south.

Commonly available in the hobby are an albino strain of *C. severum*, as well as a semi-albino (black eyes) of the same species; and a semi-albino strain of *C. nigrofasciatum*, commonly called the pink Congo or white convict. This last was developed by Kenneth Griffin of Fort Worth, Texas, although two competing fish farms have tried to assume credit for the fish. Actually, both farms received their stock from aquarist friends of Mr. Griffin, who was generous enough to pass them around. This fish is now, probably, the most popular *Cichlasoma* in the hobby.

Most of the species are hard substrate spawners, but some spawn in sand or gravel pits. In general, males and females are similarly marked, but males tend to have longer and more pointed dorsal and anal fins. A strong pair bond is established between compatible fish, and bond formation may involve display, snapping, jaw-locking, and other forms of pseudo-belligerent behavior. Generally, both parents clean the spawning site of all debris and algae, and the ends of the genitalia (genital papillae) can be observed on both parents a day or more before spawning. In the female it is blunt and in the male it is very fine and curved.

The spawning may vary from 100 to 1000 eggs, depending on the size of the parents. The territory is vigorously defended. Both parents clean the eggs and wash the newly hatched fry in their mouths. Fry, after hatching, are generally moved to one or more pits, in turn, apparently because it is easier to make up a new pit than to keep an old one clean. There are all degrees of parental care, and all degrees of ease of spawning in aquaria. For the better species,

A typical discus and angelfish habitat; the fishes take refuge among the submerged roots and branches.

Spawning of *Uaru amphiacanthoides.*

Uaru amphiacanthoides.

Cichlasoma hellabrunni is often illustrated as the smaller fish, *C. coryphaenoides.*

Cichlasoma octofasciatum, frequently called *biocellatum*.

Cichlasoma labiatum.

it is wise to employ artificial incubation of the eggs for the first or second spawning, i.e., until you are assured that you will have all the offspring you want.

Most of the recognized species (those known to the aquarist) may be kept in large community tanks with similar sized tankmates, preferably also rough cichlids. Most of them are diggers, and outside power filtration is very desirable. Earthworms are manna from heaven to all of them. Many rocks should be supplied, as well as some driftwood, and gravel for mastication purposes. A large pair of known breeders should have their own aquarium and be allowed to raise their own young, once the aquarist has satisfied his greed.

Almost all of them are ideal pond fish during the summers, and this is the way many people solve the problem of raising financially rewarding quantities of rough fish. If you have an outdoor pool, then by all means throw in a large pair of cichlids. The presence of goldfish will not stop them from populating the pool with their own kind. The only problem with most of the species is that you will raise more than you can ordinarily sell, and those that you do sell will bring a disappointingly low price. If you prefer, you can use

The color strain of *Cichlasoma nigrofasciatum* commonly called pink Congo or white convict cichlid.

Cichlasoma nigrofasciatum in normal coloration.

Cichlasoma biocellatum of aquarists, correctly *C. octofasciatum.*

Cichlasoma festivum.

Cichlasoma severum, regular type.

Cichlasoma severum, golden strain.

the fry as live food for more valuable fishes. Generally, however, it is worth your while to raise up a summer's worth, bring them to your local dealer in the Fall, and watch the expression of pain on his face.

The species in this large genus are tolerant of dirty water to a much greater extent than most other aquarium cichlids. Imports, on the other hand, should be carefully observed for animal parasites.

The genus *Aequidens*

The genus *Aequidens* Eigenmann and Bray is characterized by gills without a lobe, small gill rakers, small and moderately protractile mouth, low lateral line, and the lateral line scales being the same size as the other scales. There are a large number of species in this genus, occurring from Central to South America.

A partial listing of species would include: *awani, coeruleopunctatus, curviceps, dorsigerus, flavilabrus, freniferus, hercules, itanyi, mariae, metae, maronii, paraguayensis, portalegrensis, potaroensis, pulcher, rivulatus, sapayensis, subocularis, tetramerus, vittata,* and *zamorensis.* Also *geayi, guianensis,* and *duopunctata.*

Aequidens vittata.

Cichlasoma meeki.

Juvenile of the *Cichlasoma* species popularly known as the Jap cichlid.

Cichlasoma crassa.

These are generally considered medium sized cichlids, containing some large species *(portalegrensis)* and some dwarfs *(curviceps, hercules)*. Most are rather handsome fishes, but none are beautiful in the sense of many of the African cichlids.

Aequidens species are not generally plant uprooters, and most species can be kept in tanks with large rooted Amazon sword plants. They are hard surface spawners, and should be provided with rocks and large caves. Only the largest of them may be considered diggers, such as ports. Years ago, the port was considered one of the easiest cichlids to breed, and was extremely popular with aquarists. Today, it is hardly ever seen in shops. Another name for this fish is the black acara.

Aequidens portalegrensis often miscalled *bimaculatum.*

Young specimens of *Aequidens* are often difficult to identify, and the aquarist purchasing young fish is really taking pot luck. When grown, however, a number of species are rather distinctive, and may be identified from good aquarium photographs. See Table 9 for some data.

Aequidens awani.

Aequidens maronii.

Cichlasoma festivum spawning.

TABLE 9
Data for some species of *Aequidens* Eigenmann and Bray

	Dorsal	*Anal*	*Lateral Line*
curviceps	XV/7	III/7	23–24
hercules	XVI–XVII/8	III/6–7	26–29
mariae	XIV/9–10	III/7–8	—
metae	XIV–XV/11–12	III/8–10	—
maronii	XV/10	III/9–11	22–24
portalegrensis	XV/10	III/9	24–26
potaroensis	XIV/9–10	III/7–8	—
pulcher	XIV/10	III/8	23–25
tetramerus	XV–XVI/10	III/8–9 (10)	26–27

Aequidens pulcher.

Aequidens is better represented in western South America than *Cichlasoma*. Most of the species, however, occur well into northern South America, but not as far north as *Cichlasoma*. In Costa Rica we have only *coeruleopunctatus*; in Ecuador we have *coeruleopunctatus*, *flavilabrus*, *rivulatus*, *vittata*, *sapayensis*, *tetramerus*, and *zamorensis*. From western South America we have *hercules*, *vittata*, *freniferus*, *mariae*, *dorsigerus*, and *tetramerus*; from Venezuela we have *tetramerus* and *pulcher*, and expect (Schultz, 1949) *metae*, *mariae*, *vittata*, and *potaroensis*. The species, in general, occupy the headwaters of the Amazon in northern and western South America.

Spawning follows the usual situation as described for *Cichlasoma*. Eggs are laid on a hard surface, and should be removed for artificial incubation, except in *A. portalegrensis*, which is an exceptionally good parent. Most species do not spawn as readily as species of *Cichlasoma*, and they are not as hardy. Clean water required. They should not be mixed with very rough fishes, or are likely to suffer.

Aequidens portalegrensis.

Aequidens geayi.

Aequidens maronii.

10. ARTIFICIAL INCUBATION OF EGGS

As mentioned before, cichlid eggs may be orally brooded, or spawned and brooded on a hard surface, followed by pit brooding. Most aquarists don't incubate mouthbrooder eggs, as these lack a thick shell which probably serves an antibacterial function. We do, however, incubate sticky eggs, i.e., those laid on plants or rocks.

Item one: *get your notebook*. When a spawning is observed, check the pH, hardness, temperature, quality and quantity of light, and record these data. Other notes should also be made of the parents, colors, patterns, where and when they spawned, number and color of eggs, approximate size and shape, whether they have visible threads, etc.

Fill a clean gallon jar or two-gallon drum bowl with filtered water from the breeding aquarium. Either take advantage of an outside filter, if it is hooked up to the tank, or filter the water through a cloth net, such as one uses to strain brine shrimp. Lacking these, use a well-washed handkerchief.

Grasp the rock or leaf containing the eggs, and swirl it gently in the breeding aquarium to remove bits of debris. Lift it out of the water and place it in the jar of filtered tank water. The eggs should be hanging downward, so that the fry, upon hatching, can drop away from the patch (which may contain fungused areas). Place an airstone at the bottom of the jar, and play a gentle stream of air nearby, but not directly on the eggs. If the eggs are hanging by filaments, adjust the air so that those closest to the airstream gently bob in the current.

Add liquid methylene blue until the water is so dark that you can hardly see your hand behind the jar. Powdered dye should never be added to the brooding jar. As an alternative to methylene blue, you may use a weak solution of acriflavine (a favorite of killifish people) or a dilute solution of malachite green (used in trout hatcheries). A combination of dyes may be used, but if so, then the methylene blue should be added last. In general, methylene blue is antibacterial, and the other two dyes exert their action on fungi. But there is overlap of activities of all of them.

The intensity of the color of the methylene blue solutions in these jars represents (left) the correct dark blue color achieved by proper saturation of the water and (right) a too-weak solution which has only tinged the water light blue.

If a flowerpot, slate bar, piece of shale, or piece of petrified wood contains the eggs, it will absorb much of the dye in a day or two. More dye should be added as needed, until hatching.

The jar containing the eggs, dye, etc., is placed inside a large paper bag (supermarket type), and allowed to sit on a table or high shelf. If left on the floor, the temperature may be too low and the eggs may be killed. The bag protects the eggs from bright light, which *may* (we don't know for sure) be harmful to them.

The eggs are checked daily for progress. If fungus patches appear, these should be removed with an eye dropper. If the patches become too great, squirt the eggs off the rock onto the floor of the jar, and remove the rock with the fungused eggs. Keep the jar as clean as possible. After about 3–7 days, eggs will have hatched and the babies will be wiggling their tails furiously on the floor of the jar. In another few days, their yolk sacs will be considerably reduced, and the fry will remain upright on the floor of the jar, scooting about in circles. In another day or two, they will be able to swim, and may now be transferred into a five or ten gallon tank with clean water from the parental tank. A bare tank is best.

Aequidens itanyi.

Aequidens tetramerus.

Aequidens hercules.

Aequidens mariae.

225

Care of the fry

During these early days, the fry will appear to have little horns on their heads. These are mucus glands, and the fry will stick to various surfaces—and each other—by means of these head glands. In a few more days, they disappear. Do not feed until the yolk sac is practically gone, and the fry appear to be picking on the floor of the tank. Start the fry on microworms or, if large enough, on brine shrimp nauplii. Feed live foods only. Maintain the fry on live baby brine shrimp until they are easily large enough to take prepared foods, such as blended meats. Avoid the use of dried foods. It is important to feed the fry often on live foods during the early days to get them off to a strong start. After they have attained at least a half inch, you may taper off, feed less often, and cheaper foods (blended meats).

The fry should be transferred to larger quarters long before they seem to require those quarters. This is to speed maximum growth. A large surface to volume ratio is of considerable importance, and many breeders use special growth tanks; these are generally large and very low, giving a maximum surface area. One can construct growth tanks with wooden frames, chicken wire, and sheet plastic (which comes in large rolls, found in building supply stores). Be sure no nails or wire ends come in sharp contact with the plastic. Heavy aeration is desirable when the fry are large.

For those species which include much vegetable matter in their diets, add some hair algae, canned spinach, or cooked water sprite or duckweed. Rinse well before adding cooked vegetable material to the fry tank, and use in only slight amounts, replacing it as it is used. Keeping a light on for 24 hours a day will result in maximum growth.

11. DISEASES OF CICHLIDS

In the aquarium, cichlids are susceptible to the usual diseases associated with tropical fishes, i.e., ich, velvet, fin and body fungus, pop-eye, fin-rot, etc. Pet shops have a wide range of medicines with which to fight these disease conditions. In nature, however, cichlids are found with certain diseases associated with the particular environment in that part of the world. Sometimes we see imported fishes that have brought in these diseases. In the case of many parasitic animal diseases, there is no chance of the disease cycle being carried through in the aquarium. Nonetheless, the presence of exotic parasites is intriguing, and we might look at some of the things our charges may bring in with them.

An intelligent approach to diseases requires that we learn two things: classification of organisms, and the rationality of chemotherapy. To begin, we can state that aquarium diseases fall into two general categories: those caused by microbes (viruses, bacteria, fungi) and those caused by parasitic animals. Intermediate is the case of velvet disease *(Oodinium)*, caused by a parasitic single-celled alga. For viruses there are no cures, but few viruses are known to attack cichlids. One outstanding exception is the case of *Lymphocystis* virus. The unusual aspect of lymphocystis is that it causes the infected cells to greatly enlarge, so that these cells become visible to the naked eye. Infection is, however, not usually considered fatal and the disease is more of biological interest than it is dangerous. Found on many kinds of fishes, it is also known from the cichlid *Cichlasoma synspilum* collected in Guatemala. For additional information on lymphocystis, see Wolf (1964), Wolf *et al.* (1966), and Weissenberg (1965a, 1965b).

Fungus diseases are not that common on cichlids. Some of the diseases called *fungus* by aquarists are really filament-forming chains of bacteria. This is of major importance, as fungus diseases are very difficult to cure. The fungus *Ichthyophonus* is reported to be a major cause of death of aquarium fishes, but I think it is very over-rated, and somewhat uncommon. This organism attacks the internal

Aequidens curviceps pair select and prepare a site for spawning.

The female depositing eggs, and on facing page the male approaches to fertilize them.

Aequidens curviceps and spawn.

organs of fishes, is not very specific toward either organs or hosts, and may occur in any fish. For diagnosis of a death due to no other obvious causes, slit open the fish and find its liver. Feel the liver with your fingers. If it feels sandy, you can suspect *Ichthyophonus*.

Every serious aquarist has a cheap microscope at least. These are available at toy stores for five to ten dollars each. The low power of such microscopes is adequate for most things an aquarist needs to examine. Take a small piece of the liver (or other organs if desired) and place it on a glass microscope slide. Place a cover glass on top of it, and crush the liver very well. Examine under the microscope. You can add aquarium dyes if you like to color the specimen. Methylene blue, malachite green, acriflavine, and Mercurochrome work fine either individually or in various combinations. Draw what you see in your notebook. You may find other fungus disease organisms, or even various parasitic protozoa. If you are reasonably sure that you have *Ichthyophonus*, you will need phenoxyethanol, a drug that you can purchase at any chemical supply or surgical supply house (see your Yellow Pages). It is very inexpensive, about $2.50 for a 250 gram bottle of the liquid. While you are there, also buy some 1, 5, and 10 milliliter (ml) glass pipettes. Add 10 ml of drug to a quart of hot tap water, and stir vigorously or mix in a blender. Store in the dark until needed. This amount will treat 10 gallons of aquarium water, and is a maximal dose. The dose should be added gradually, about $\frac{1}{3}$ every 12 hours. In short, you will treat with *up to* 1 ml per gallon, but the drug must be dissolved in a large volume of hot water in order to get it into solution.

Ichthyophonus disease is contagious. The carcass of a dead victim is the source of further infections. Thus, if you remove fish that are dying, rather than waiting until they are dead, you will be avoiding the danger of infecting additional tankmates with *Ichthyophonus*, assuming that it was the cause of death.

Bacterial diseases are numerous, frequently fatal, and generally fast-developing. For simplicity, we will classify bacteria on their staining characteristics: Group 1 **acid-fast.** Group 2 **gram-negative.** Group 3 **gram-positive.** You see that we have used two staining tests, the Gram stain and Acid-fast stain. You don't have to do this yourself, as will become apparent. Slow-healing or slow-progressing sores on the body of fishes, sometimes with bleeding, are often due to acid-fast bacteria. As this most often occurs on old, sickly fish, they are not worth treating and should be isolated until they recover or die. If such sores are found on young fish, they may be due to other causes and should be treated with medications for gram-negative organisms. Why gram-negative? Because these are the most common fish pathogens. In fact, about the only gram-positive organisms you need to worry about are the bacilli (rod-shaped bacteria) that cause whitish filaments to grow on your fish. Of course, you cannot tell if these filaments are true bacteria or *Saprolegnia* fungi (fungi that frequently grow on dead fish eggs and in open wounds). But since the filaments must be one or the other, swab the tuft with Mercurochrome and treat the tank with penicillin. Penicillin works specifically on gram-positive bacteria by preventing them from forming normal cellular walls to support the cell. In the presence of penicillin, the walls are deficient, weak, and the pressure of the cell causes it to burst.

Most fish disease bacteria are gram-negative cells called *pseudomonads* and *aeromonads*. You can use anything except penicillin on them to kill them. Their cell walls are made differently and penicillin has no effect. You can interfere with their vitamin requirements by using sulfa drugs, or with protein synthesis by using tetracyclines, chloramphenicol or streptomycin. All living things must have their protein constantly replaced, and these drugs generally act as structural analogues of normal compounds. That is to say, the drug resembles something normal that they use, but when they pick up the drug molecule by mistake, their machinery becomes fouled up. Note the similarity between para-amino-benzoic acid (a normal enzyme precursor) and sulfanilamide. Don't bother with dyes, metals or salts. For bacterial diseases you should use only antibiotics. And use one at a time, so that you will learn which drug will cure which disease. Then, the next time you have the problem, you won't waste time trying all the wrong things.

One exception to the use of dyes is malachite green. This dye has been reported to have both antibacterial and antifungal action. See Lanzing (1965). For a monographic treatment of fish microbiology, see volume 5 of *Developments in Industrial Microbiology*, pages 97–148, published by the American Institute of Biological Sciences, 1964, for a group of six review articles.

Cichlids are frequently afflicted with superficial (meaning *skin*, not meaning *unimportant*) diseases. The two most common diseases

Aequidens pulcher spawning.

Principles of antibiotic chemotherapy: (1) *para-amino-sulfanilic acid* ('sulfanilamide') is an antibiotic that fools bacteria into thinking they are getting (2) *para-amino-benzoic acid*, a substance they require for normal functioning. (3) *Chloramphenicol* is required to interfere with bacterial protein synthesis, but is a dangerous drug for humans, and only used in emergency situations. (4) *Penicillin* occurs in several forms, where the -R- group may be varied. It interferes with bacterial cell wall synthesis. (5) *Tetracylines* also occur in several forms, and inhibit protein synthesis. (6) *Streptomycins* cause bacteria to mis-read their genetic instructions and make mistakes in protein synthesis.

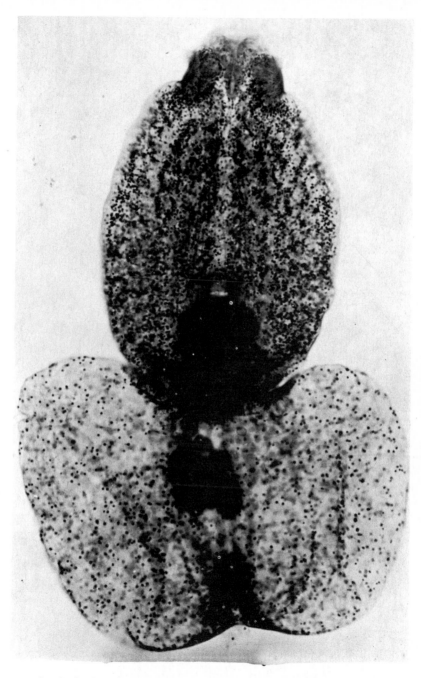

Larva of a fluke found in an imported *Symphysodon*. Such parasites are never found in tank-bred fish.

Cichlasoma meeki spawning and guarding fry.

are velvet and white spot disease (*Ichthyophthirius* or Ich). Both may be treated with malachite green, 0.75% aqueous solution, one drop per gallon, repeated in 24 hours. Velvet also responds to copper treatment, and you can either use a commercial copper remedy or place a copper scouring sponge in the tank until the velvet or dust disappears. For Ich and other superficial infections, you may prefer to use formalin, 4 drops per gallon. Commercial formalin is used, and it is usually labeled 37% or 40% formaldehyde. Don't cut it, but use it dropwise. Formalin is widely used in hatcheries for all kinds of superficial diseases, from protozoa to worms.

Arthropods infect many cichlids in nature. They may attack the whole body surface (*Argulus*, or fish louse), the gills (*Ergasilus*), or be buried deep in the flesh (*Lernea* and other anchor worms). For deeply imbedded anchor worms, all you can do is cut the parasite with a scissors and hope the dead remainder doesn't cause a bacterial infection. There is some slight chance of contagion, so the tank should be treated as for other arthropods. To clear up arthropod infestation (*Argulus*, *Ergasilus*, etc.), treat the tank with a fresh solution of potassium permanganate. The dose is very variable, depending on the pH, the age of the dye, and other factors. See any disease handbook. Plants and snails are killed by this treatment. *Do not remove arthropods from the tank by hand.* It's better if you leave them there *so that you can tell when you've added enough dye to kill them.*

If your fish have white, yellow, or black lumps in the skin and fins, you can assume that they are caused by the presence of larval worms. These cysts may be picked out with a needle, or may be left. They very rarely cause any real disease, are not contagious in the aquarium, and in general should be left alone. They may increase in size, but not in number. If close to the eye or another questionable region, prick them out with a needle (dipped in whiskey), and swab the wound with Mercurochrome. Isolate the fish in order to avoid its tankmates biting the wound.

Cichlids may suffer from internal flukes, which we can ignore as they are seldom dangerous, and very difficult to identify. They may also suffer from superficial flukes (Monogenea) on the skin and/or gills. These usually multiply rapidly, and are dangerous. You can suspect superficial flukes if the fish constantly scratch themselves, breath rapidly and with widely flared gill covers, are irritable, and have red spots on the body. A microscopic examination of skin scrapings is very valuable. Treatment is with formalin, four drops per gallon. Even if protozoa were the cause, rather than flukes, the formalin will clear it up. You can get formalin from your physician, or a supply house.

There are many exotic parasites occurring in or on cichlids in nature, but they only rarely are found in imported material. Probably the collectors discard such fishes. Sometimes, however, some beautiful (to me!) parasites are indeed found. A case in point is the finding of an internal isopod in the discus fish, and other cichlids. See my report in *Aquarium Illustrated*, vol. 1, no. 3, pp. 34–35, May–June, 1966. This arthropod, *Artystone trysibia*, occurs in the body cavity of *Symphysodon discus*, *Geophagus brasiliensis*, and *Crenicichla lacustris*, as well as in other non-cichlid fishes. It probably can occur in almost any fairly large South American cichlid. Eventually it breaks a small hole in the body wall, and soon causes the death of the host. A similar parasite occurs in Asian fishes, but in that case there are always a pair of isopods in each cyst.

A few tables will suffice to indicate what is known of natural parasites of cichlids. It will be immediately obvious to all advanced aquarists that the parasites of cichlids have hardly been looked at. Practically, only the commercially important *Tilapia* species have been examined in depth, and except for a very few other cichlids, this branch of parasitology is a wide open field. I like to point out these types of information to the naïve and depressed graduate student who thinks that everything of interest has already been done!

The hole-in-the-head disease of discus and some other cichlids deserves special attention. See the section on discus fish.

Cichlasoma nigrofasciatum as occurring in natural habitat.

Pink color variation of *Cichlasoma nigrofasciatum*.

TABLE 11
Monogenetic trematodes from cichlids

New World Cichlids
  Aequidens maroni — *Urocleidus cavanaughi, Urocleidus aequidens.*
  Pterophyllum scalare — *Gussevia spiralocirra.*
Old *World Cichlids*
  Tilapia species — *Cichlidogyrus cirratus, C. tilapiae, C. bifurcatus, C. arthracanthus, C. tiberianus, Enterogyrus cichlidarum, Cleidodiscus halli, Gyrodactylus cichlidarum.*
  Hemichromis species — *Cichlidogyrus dioncus, C. longicirrus, C. bychowskii, Onchobdella voltensis, O. spirocirra, O. pterigyalis, O. aframae.*
  Pelmatochromis guentheri — *Onchobdella krachii.*

TABLE 12
Arthropods from cichlids

New World Cichlids
  Symphysodon discus — *Artystone trysibia.*
  Geophagus brasiliensis — *Artystone trysibia.*
  Crenicichla species — *Artystone trysibia, Dolops gaeyi.*
  Cichlasoma species — *Argulus chromidis, A. cubensis.*
  Aequidens species — *Dolops gaeyi.*
Old *World Cichlids*
  Tilapia species — *Lamproglena monodi, Ergasilus* sp., *Argulus japonicus, A. rhipidiophorus, A. africanus, A.* spp., *Lernea cyprinacea.*
  Pelmatochromis congicus — *Ergasilus cunningtoni, E. kandti, E. megacheir.*
  Haplochromis chrysonotus — *Lernaea palati*
  H. nkatae — *L. palati*
  Tylochromis mylodon — *Ergasilus sarsi*
  Cichlidae of Africa — *Lamproglena monodi*

242

TABLE 13
Digenetic trematodes of cichlids

Trematodes	Hosts	Locations
Plagioporus biliaris	Haplochromis sp.	bile duct, gall bladder
Bolbophorus sp.	Tilapia spp.	muscles, skin?
Clonorchis sp.	Tilapia spp.	muscles, skin
Clinostomum spp.	Tilapia spp.	muscles, skin
Euclinostomum sp.	Tilapia spp.	muscles, skin
Haplorchis sp.	Tilapia spp.	muscles, skin
	Haplochromis spp.	muscles, skin
Neochasmus sp.	Tilapia spp.	muscles, skin
Pygidiopsis sp.	Tilapia spp.	muscles, fat tissues
Stictodora sp.	Tilapia spp.	muscles
Centrocestus sp.	Tilapia spp.	gills
Transversotrema sp.	Tilapia spp.	under scales
Allocreadium spp.	Aequidens pulcher, Crenicichla geayi	intestine
Crassicutis cichlasomae	Cichlasoma mayorum	stomach
Trematobrien haplochromios	Haplochromis moffati	intestine

TABLE 14
Nematodes (roundworms) of cichlids

Nematodes	Hosts	Locations
Contracaecum spp.	Tilapia spp.	skin
Zeylanicobdella sp.	Tilapia spp.	—
Rhabdochona denudata	Tilapia spp.	intestine
Asymphylodora tincae	Haplochromis sp.	intestine
	Tilapia spp.	intestine
Capillaria pterophylli	Pterophyllum scalare	intestine
Gendria tilapiae	Tilapia galilaea	intestine

TABLE 15
Tapeworms of Cichlids

Cichla ocellaris	Proteocephalus microscopius	Brazil
C. monoculus	P. macrophallus	Brazil
Tilapia sp.	P. bivitellatus	Sierra Leone
Aequidens portalegrensis	Bothriocephalus musculosus	aquarium

TABLE 16
Thorny-headed worms (Acanthocephala) from Cichlids

Aequidens pulcher	Pandosentis iracundus
Crenicichla geayi	P. iracundus, Quadrigyrus torquatus
Tilapia spp.	Acanthosentis tilapiae

12. SECURING TECHNICAL LITERATURE

A number of the papers on cichlids contain information that an aquarist will have no difficulty understanding. How do you get them? Go to your local college, and have a student point you to the library. Ask the librarian to direct you to the science section. Have a list of the articles you want to see, cited exactly as they are in the bibliography. Use the card catalogue to find the journals you want. If you have any trouble, feel free to ask the librarians for help. That's what they are there for.

If the library does not carry the journal you want, ask the librarian about interlibrary loan service. For a very small fee, you will be able to purchase a photostat of the article you want. Rates run from 5 to 10 cents a page. If you are a student, you may be able to borrow the journal on interlibrary loan service and avoid the cost of making a copy of the article. In that case, you will just pay for postage to get the journal from wherever it is to the local library. Interlibrary loan service is non-profit, and is a service designed primarily for researchers.

To find new literature on cichlids, look for the journal *Biological Abstracts*. This comes out every two weeks or so, and lists papers and their abstracts from all branches of biology. Turn to the back few pages, and you will find the section on fishes. It's always fun to find new and interesting papers on cichlids or other tropical fishes. And you will learn a lot about how hard ichthyologists are working, in part to benefit you, the aquarist. Now that you've read this book, rest a while, and read it again next month. Perhaps you can add something.

BIBLIOGRAPHY

Aronson, L. R. 1948. Problems in the behavior and physiology of a species of African mouthbreeding fish. Trans. N.Y. Acad. Sci. ser. 2, *11* (2): 33–42.

Baerends, G. P. and Baerends, J. M. 1950. An introduction to the study of the ethology of cichlid fishes. Behavior, suppl. 1: 1–242.

Beauchamp, R. S. A. 1964. The Rift Valley Lakes of Africa. Verh. Intern. Verein. Limnol. *15*: 91–99.

Blum, V. 1968a. Die Auslösung des Laichreflexes durch Reserpin bei dem südamerikanischen Buntbarsch *Pterophyllum scalare*. Z. f. vergl. Physiol. *60*: 79–81.

—— 1968b. Experimente zum Steuerungsmechanismus hormoninduzierter Brutpflegereaktionen beim Buntbarsch *Pterophyllum scalare*. Z. f. vergl. Physiol. *61*: 21–33.

—— and Fiedler, K. 1965. Hormonal control of reproductive behavior in some cichlid fish. Gen. Comp. Endocrinol. *5*: 186–196.

Burchard, J., Jr. and Wickler, W. 1965. Eine neue Form des Cichliden *Hemichromis fasciatus* Peters. Z. Zool. Syst. Evolutionsforsch. *3*: 227–283.

Bussing, W. A. 1967. New species and new records of Costa Rican freshwater fishes with a tentative list of species. Rev. Biol. Trop. *14* (2): 205–249.

Coe, M. J. 1966. The biology of *Tilapia grahami* Boulenger in Lake Magadi, Kenya. Acta Tropica *23* (2): 146–177.

Dadzie, S. 1968. The structure of the chorion of the egg of the mouthbrooding cichlid fish *Tilapia mossambica*. J. Zool., Lond. *154*: 161–163.

Eckstein, B. and Spira, M. 1966. Sterilization of the cichlid fish Tilapia aurea. Israel J. Zool. *15*: 31.

Eibl-Eibesfeldt, I., and Kramer, S. 1958. Ethology, the comparative study of animal behavior. Quart. Rev. Biol. *33* (3): 181–211.

Eigenmann, C. H. and Allen, W. R. 1942. Fishes of Western South America. Waverly Press, 494 p. + map.

—— and Eigenmann, R. S. 1891. A catalogue of the freshwater fishes of South America. Proc. U.S.N.M. *14*: 1–81.

Fishelson, V. L. 1966. Untersuchungen zur vergleichenden Entwicklungsgeschichte der Gattung *Tilapia*. Zool. Jb. Anat. *83*: 571–656.

—— 1967. Cichlidae of the genus *Tilapia* in Israel. Bamidgeh. *18*: 67–80.

Fowler, H. W. 1937. A collection of Haitian fishes obtained by Mr. Stanley Woodward. Proc. Acad. Nat. Sci. Phila. *89*: 309–315.

—— 1938. A smaller collection of freshwater fishes from eastern Cuba. Op. cit. *90*: 143–147.

—— 1939. A collection of fishes obtained by Mr. William C. Morrow in the Ucayali River basin, Peru. Op. cit. *91*: 219–289.

—— 1940. Zoological results of the second Bolivian expedition, 1936–1937. Part 1. The Fishes. Op. cit. *92*: 43–103.

—— 1944. Freshwater fishes from Northwestern Colombia. Op. cit. *96*: 227–248.

Fryer, G. 1959. The trophic interrelationships and ecology of some littoral communities of Lake Nyasa with especial reference to the fishes, and a discussion of the evolution of a group of rock-frequenting Cichlidae Proc. Zool. Soc. Lond. *132*: 153–281.

—— 1957. A new species of *Gephyrochromis* from Lake Nyasa, with notes on its ecology and affinities. Rev. Zool. Bot. Afr. *55*: 347–352.

—— 1964. Further studies on the parasitic crustacea of African freshwater fishes. Proc. Zool. Soc. London. *143*: 79–102.

—— Greenwood, P. H. and Trewavas, E. 1955. Scale-eating habits of African cichlid fishes. Nature *175*: 1089.

—— and Iles, T. D. 1955. Predation pressure and evolution in Lake Nyasa. Nature *176*: 470.

Goldstein, R. J. 1967. *Nannacara anomala*. Aquarium *36* (1): 6 ff.

Greenberg, B., Zijlstra, J. J. and Baerend, G. P. 1965. A quantitative description of the behavior changes during the reproductive cycle of the cichlid fish *Aequidens portalegrensis* Hensel. Koninkl. Nederl. Akad. van Wetenschappen-Amsterdam, Proc., Ser. C., *68*: 135–149.

Greenwood, P. H. 1964. Explosive speciation in African lakes. Proc. Roy. Inst. Gr. Brit. *40* (III, 184): 256–269.

—— 1965. Two new species of *Haplochromis* from Lake Victoria. Ann. Mag. Nat. Hist. ser. 13, *8*: 303–318, pl. XI.

—— Rosen, D. E., Weitzman, S. H. and Myers, G. S. 1966. Phyletic studies of teleostean fishes, with a provisional classification of living forms. Bull. Amer. Mus. Nat. Hist. *131* (4): 339–456.

Heiligenberg, W. 1965a. A quantitative analysis of digging movements and their relationship to aggressive behavior in cichlids. Anim. Behav. *13*: 163–170.

—— 1965b. Color polymorphism in the males of an African cichlid fish. J. Zool. *146*: 95–97.

—— 1965c. The suppression of behavioral activities by frightening stimuli. Z.f. vergl. Physiol. *50*: 660–672.

Innes, W. T. 1951. Exotic Aquarium Fishes, 12 ed., Innes Publ. Co., Phila., 521 p.

Kiener, A. and Maugé, M. 1966. Contributions a l'étude systematique et écologique des poissons cichlidae endémiques de Madagascar. Mem. Mus. Nat. Hist. Nat., Nouv. ser. *40* (2): 4–99, 4 pl.

Kleinhout, J. 1965. On experiments with Yohimbine on the jewel fish, *Hemichromis maculatus*. Zool. Anz. *174*: 399–400.

Kohn, A. and Paperna, I. 1964. Monogenetic trematodes from aquarium fishes. Rev. Brasil. Biol. *24*: 145–149.

Kuenzer, P. 1962a. Wie erkennen Cichliden-Junge ihre Eltern? I. D.A.T.Z. *15* (11): 332–334.

—— 1962b. Wie erkennen Cichliden-Junge ihre Eltern? II. D.A.T.Z. *15* (12): 362–365.

—— 1962c. Die Auslösung der Nachfolgereaktion durch Bewegungsreize bei Jungfischen von *Nannacara anomala* Regan. Naturwissenschaften *49* (22): 525–526.

—— 1964. Weitere Versuche zur Auslösung der Nachfolgereaktion bei Jungfischen von *Nannacara anomala*. Naturwissenschaften *51*: 419–420.

—— 1965. Zur optischen Auslösung von Brutpflegehandlungen bei *Nannacara anomala* weibchenen. Naturwissenschaften *52*: 19–20.

Kühme, W. 1964a. Eine chemisch ausgelöste Brutpflegereaktion bei Cichliden. Naturwissenschaften *51*: 20–21.

—— 1964b. Eine chemisch ausgelöste Schwarmreaktion bei jungen Cichliden. Naturwissenschaften *51*: 120–121.

Lanzing, W. J. R. 1965. Observations on malachite green in relation to its application to fish diseases. Hydrobiologia *25*: 426–440.

Loiselle, P. V. 1967. The cupido cichlid. Aquar. Illustr. *2* (3): 16–23.

Lowe, R. H. 1959. Breeding behavior patterns and ecological differences between *Tilapia* species and their significance for evolution within the genus *Tilapia*. Proc. Zool. Soc., Lond. *132*: 1–30.

—— 1969. The cichlid fishes of Guyana, South America, with notes on their ecology and breeding behaviour. Zool. J. Linn. Soc. *48*: 255–302.

Meinken, H. 1965. Eine neue *Apistogramma*-Art aus Venezuela. Senckenbergiana Biol. *46* (4): 257–263.

Myrberg, A. A., Jr. 1965. A descriptive analysis of the behavior of the African cichlid fish, *Pelmatochromis guentheri* (Sauvage). Anim. Behav. *13*: 312–329.

—— 1966. Parental recognition of young in cichlid fishes. Anim. Behav. *14*: 565–571.

—— Kramer, E. and Heinecke, P. 1965. Sound production by cichlid fishes. Science *149* (3683): 555–558.

Ouchynnyk, M. M. 1968. Annotated list of the freshwater fish of Ecuador. Zool. Anz. *181*: 237–268.

Paperna, I. 1960. Studies on monogenetic trematodes in Israel. 2. Monogenetic trematodes of cichlids. Bamidgeh *12*: 20–33.

—— 1963. *Enterogyrus cichlidarum* n. gen. n. sp., a monogenetic trematode parasitic in the intestine of a fish. Bull. Res. Council of Israel, sec. B., zool., *11B*: 183–187.

—— 1965. Monogenetic trematodes collected from freshwater fish in southern Ghana. Bamidgeh *17*: 107–111.

—— 1968a. Monogenetic trematodes collected from freshwater fish in Ghana. Second report. Bamidgeh *20*: 88–100.

—— 1968b. *Onchobdella* n. gen. New genus of monogenetic trematodes (Dactylogyridae, Bychowski 1933) from cichlid fish from West Africa. Proc. Helm. Soc. Washington *35*: 200–206.

Parvatheswararao, V. 1967. Some mechanisms underlying thermal acclimation in a freshwater fish, *Etroplus maculatus*. Comp. Biochem. Physiol. *21*: 619–626.

Peters, H. M. 1965a. Angeborenes Verhalten bei Buntbarschen. I. Wege der Analyse. Umschau *21*: 665–670.

—— 1965b. Angeborenes Verhalten bei Buntbarschen. II. Das.Problem der erblichen Grundlage des Kontaktverhaltens. Umschau *22*: 711–718.

Price, C. E. 1966. *Urocleidus cavanaughi*, a new monogenetic trematode from the gills of the keyhole cichlid, *Aequidens maroni* (Steindachner). Bull. Ga. Acad. Sci. *24*: 117–120.

—— 1967a. The freshwater monogenetic trematodes of South America. Rev. di Parassit. *28*: 87–95.

—— 1967b. The freshwater monogenetic trematodes of Africa. Rev. Zool. Bot. Afr. *76*: 375–391.

—— and Schlueter, E. A. 1968. Two new monogenetic trematodes from South America. J. Tenn. Acad. Sci. for 1968: 23–25.

Regan, C. T. 1921. The cichlid fishes of Lake Nyassa. Proc. Zool. Soc. Lond. *91*: 675–727.

—— 1922. The cichlid fishes of Lake Victoria. Proc. Zool. Soc. Lond. *92*: 157–191.

Richter, H. J. 1969. *Nannochromis nudiceps*. Trop. Fish Hobbyist *17* (5): 36 ff.

Ruwet, J. C. 1968. Familial behavior of *Tilapia* and its implications. Nature *217* (5132): 977.

Sivadas, P. 1965. Absorption of fat in the alimentary canal of *Tilapia mossambica*. J. Cellul. Comp. Physiol. *65* (2): 249–253.

Schultz, L. P. 1949. A further contribution to the ichthyology of Venezuela. Proc. U.S.N.M. *99*: 1–211, pl. 1–3.

—— 1967. Review of South American freshwater angelfishes—genus *Pterophyllum*. Proc. U.S.N.M. *120*: 1–10.

Sterba, G. 1959. Freshwater Fishes of the World, Viking Press, New York, 878 p.

Thys van den Audenaerde, D. 1968. A preliminary contribution to a systematic revision of the genus *Pelmatochromis* Hubrecht sensu lato. Rev. Zool. Bot. Afr. *77*: 351–391.

Trewavas, E. 1935. A synopsis of the cichlid fishes of Lake Nyasa. Ann. Mag. Nat. Hist. (10) *16*: 65–118.

—— 1946. The types of cichlid fishes described by Borodin in 1931 and 1936, and of two species described by Boulenger in 1901. Proc. Zool. Soc. Lond. *116*: 240–246.

—— 1966. *Tilapia aurea* (Steindachner) and the status of *Tilapia nilotica exul*, *T. monodi* and *T. lemassoni*. Israel J. Zool. *14*: 258–276.

Ward, J. A. and Barlow, G. W. 1967. The maturation and regulation of glancing off the parents by young orange chromides (*Etroplus maculatus*). Behaviour *29* (1): 1–56.

Weissenberg, R. 1965a. Fifty years of research on the Lymphocystis virus disease of fishes (1914–1964). Ann. N.Y. Acad. Sci. *126*: 362–374.

—— 1965b. Morphological studies on Lymphocystis tumor cells of a cichlid from Guatemala, *Cichlasoma synspilum* Hubbs. Ann. N.Y. Acad. Sci. *126*: 396–413.

Wickler, W. 1965. Neue Varianten des Fortpflanzungsverhaltens afrikanischer Cichliden. Naturwissenschaften *52*: 219.

—— 1966a. Naturliche Ubersexualisierung des Soziallebens beim Brabantbuntbarsch. Umschau Wiss. Tech. *66* (17): 571–572.

—— 1966b. Sexualdimorphismus, Paarbildung und Versteckbrüten bei Cichliden. Zool. Jb. Syst. *93*: 127–138.

—— 1966c. Mimicry in tropical fishes. Phil. Trans. Roy. Soc. Lond., B, *251*: 473–474.

Wolf, K. 1964. Lymphocystis disease of fish (revised). Fishery leaflet 565, U.S. Dept. of the Interior: 1–4.

—— Gravell, M., and Malsberger, R. G. 1966. Lymphocystis virus: Isolation and propagation in centrarchid fish cell lines. Science *151* (3713): 1004–1005.

INDEX

Page reference numbers set in
bold face refer to illustrations.

252